Female Banded Demoiselle lunches by the Wye

Published by Hereford Biological Records Centre
P.O. Box 144
Hereford
HR1 2YH
Email: hbrc@herefordshire.gov.uk

Role of Herefordshire Biological Records Centre

- To acquire, store and manage records and information about the flora, fauna, habitats and sites of biological, ecological, geological and geomorphological interest in Herefordshire.
- To promote and support well planned and locally relevant survey and monitoring.
- To promote agreed data standards and to help and encourage recorders achieve these.
- To support users by providing access to relevant data and information held by the Centre.

HBRC is a partnership project

Herefordshire Biological Records Centre wishes to acknowledge
the financial support of Herefordshire Council and English Nature

Dragonflies of Herefordshire

by Peter Garner

[handwritten inscription: "To Dad/Sue Here's some of what I've been upto. Steve x"]

Photographs

Les Clarke and Peter Garner

Contributions

The chapter on "The Life-cycle and larval stages" – Steve Roe

Published by Herefordshire Biological Records Centre 2005

ISBN 978-0-9551880-0-8

Special thank you to Steve Roe
(The Hereford Biological Record Centre Manager
for the collating of records and production of the maps)

Contents

The former Mathon Gravel Pit between Mathon and Coddington is now a private fishing lake.
This view, with the Malvern Hills in the background, includes my home in the centre
of the distant row of properties, from where I can look out over Herefordshire.

Introduction and Acknowledgments

Filling the "Black Hole"

When I moved to the eastern edge of Herefordshire in 1985 I had been recording dragonflies in Worcestershire for six years. My interest, in common with many other naturalists, had been stimulated by Cyril Hammond's publication of 'The Dragonflies of Great Britain and Ireland'[1] and then with the launch of The British Dragonfly Society[2] in 1983 I was hooked! I should also acknowledge early encouragement and guidance from my close friend Roger Maskew.

The inspiration for my recording of Odonata in Herefordshire was Tony Fox whom I contacted through the 'Odonata Recording Scheme'. When Tony wrote to me in March 1989, in response to a batch of records I had sent to him from 1987 and 1988, he explained that the Biological Records Centre at Monks Wood had records of only 15 species for VC36 (Vice County Herefordshire) and he described the County as a 'black hole'. In subsequent correspondence he apologised for this derogatory term and assured me he was referring solely to a black hole in terms of odonata recording!

The vast majority of records are mine. As a lone recorder in a county which covers 537,000 acres, the coverage is far from perfect. Unfortunately, I have not been able to indulge my love of natural history in the way of Victorian vicars and doctors, but as a headteacher, I have benefited, each year, from about eight weeks of school holidays falling within the recording period for dragonflies. Most of my available recording time has been in late July and August, and as a result those species, such as the Hawkers and Darters, that are most numerous towards the end of the summer, are better recorded than the earlier flying Chasers, the Club-tailed, and some of the Damselflies.

Most records that are not my own have come from local people who have taken a special interest in their own garden or farm pond. In the case of Phyll and Richard King, who have created on their small-holding near Little Dewchurch one of the finest small dragonfly ponds in the county[3], their careful record taking has not only provided some of the earliest emergence records for Herefordshire, but it has encouraged them to record further afield as well. They have made a systematic search along the banks of the Wye near Hoarwithy for Club-tailed Dragonfly exuviae and I include details of their research under the main species account for Club-tailed Dragonfly.

Will Watson is a wild life consultant with specialist knowledge of amphibians. While carrying out survey work for the Herefordshire Ponds and Newts Project[4] and generally recording for HART (Herefordshire Amphibian and Reptile Team) he has sent me records of dragonflies and damselflies present at the ponds he has visited.

Mike Averill who is the BDS recorder for the Midlands, and who has written an account of the Dragonflies of Worcestershire[5] has contributed several records from sites in the east of the county close to the Worcestershire border. Mike has also advised Phyll and Richard King on their Club-tailed Dragonfly research at Hoarwithy.

Michael Bradley is a Gloucestershire recorder who has contributed several valuable records from the southwest corner of Herefordshire where the influence of the Forest of Dean

1 Hammond C.O. (1977)
2 For further deails of the BDS please contact the Secretary, WH Wain, The Haywain, Hollywater Road, Bordon, Hants GU35 0AD
3 Woodlea, Little Dewchurch (SO5432) (see photo page 13)
4 One of several projects organised by the Herefordshire Rivers Leader+ Programme
5 Averill, M. (1996)

has resulted in a couple of records for the Golden-ringed Dragonfly, which otherwise seems reluctant to venture far from the Black Mountains (the full list of contributors is appended)

This book is not intended as a field guide; there are plenty of excellent editions which are listed in the biography at the back, but I do include a descriptive section under each species account: suggestions are made as to what to look out for and at times I attempt to enthuse the reader by sharing some of the excitement evoked by these dramatic and exquisitely beautiful insects.

I have also included field notes, whether relating to behaviour or appearance, which, as far as I know, are not contained in any other publications. The art of the naturalist is chiefly one of observation and anyone who has spent as many hours as I have watching dragonflies would be expected to make some original observations. It is possible that some of these observations are peculiar to Herefordshire Dragonflies – where that is the case, there can be no greater justification for publishing a local study.

I make no apology for the lack of balance in the species accounts: where I have plenty to say I have not curtailed my writing, but where the observations are few or of modest interest I have been brief.

Specific help in compiling this book has come from:

Steve Roe – who has organised the collation of records and produced all the maps. Steve has also written the chapter on the 'Natural History of Dragonflies'. Furthermore, without Steve's help in securing generous financial support through the Hereford Biological Record Centre, this publication could not have taken place.

Finally I'd like to thank Steve and the volunteer helpers at The Record Centre for the many tasks of publishing, advertising and distributing this book.

Steve has been supported in the Record Centre by Heather Webster and Helen Forster. **Les Clarke** has contributed half of all the photographs contained in this book. Les' photographs are initialled with a discreet LC, mine with the initials PGG and those taken by Phill King with PK. **Chris Harris** contributed the picture of a Male Common Darter on page 124. **Will Watson** gave me valuable support when writing the 'Ponds' section of the Habitat chapter. I used an article Will had written about Herefordshire Ponds for the "HART website" as a starting point.

Alison Holmes and staff at Reprodux Printers Ltd. have been exceedingly patient, very helpful and creative with suggested improvements.

My son **Tom Garner** has helped with the drawings accompanying the Life-cycle chapter and the anatomy and glossary pages.

Tom has also designed the front cover from a photograph that I took of Emerald Damselflies.

Anthea Brian, Steve Roe, Mike Averill, Roger Maskew, Dr. John Ross, Jackie Denovan and Ann Wilkinson, have all given generously of their time as proof-readers. I am especially grateful to Mike Averill for his mentoring guidance as the author of *The Dragonflies of Worcestershire* and the B.D.S. recorder for the Midlands, his support has allowed me to avoid some errors and as a result given the book greater authority.

Finally, I should like to recognise the support I have always received from my **wife Lynne**, throughout the 20 years of recording and the many late nights writing, during the last two years. Lynne has been understanding and encouraging when I have gone recording on my own, but on many glorious sunny days we have ventured forth together and felt hugely privileged to share some of the most wonderful pond sites and riverside walks anyone could ever wish to visit.

Records during the recording period 1987 - 2005 have been received from:

Mike Averill
David Bows
Michael Bradley
Anthea Brian
John Day
Mary Ford
Beryl Harding
Michael Harper
Chris Harris
Ian Hart
Rob Havard
Bob Kemp (via Alex Lockton)
Phyll and Richard King
Roger Maskew

Matthew Oates
Nicholas Reuss
Steve Roe
Jeremy Russell
Cyril Sheldrake
Tony Simpson
Janet Stevenson
Jane Sweetman
Tony Thorlby
Pete Tierney
John Voysey
Will Watson
Chris Wells
Mike Williams

PGG

Emerald Damselfly – female resting on Bracken

9

History of Recording

This section is naturally short because, as I explained in my introduction, very little recording of Dragonflies in Herefordshire had taken place before I started in 1986. Just 15 species had been identified in the county, mostly by naturalists who were specialists in other fields.

The earliest reference I can find connecting Dragonflies and Herefordshire is for Banded Demoiselle near Symond's Yat, Herefordshire, recorded by W.J. Lucas in his book *British Dragonflies*, published in 1900. *British Dragonflies*, by Lucas is the first book published on this subject and there is just this one reference made to Herefordshire.

In *"Herefordshire"*, *(chapters written to celebrate the centenary of the Woolhope Naturalists Field Club – 1954)* the chapter on "Herefordshire Insects" lists 14 species of "the order Odonata" – dragonflies and damselflies. The earliest date is 1902 for the Large Red Damselfly, which is one of several records from John Henry Wood (1841-1914) who was primarily a moth and fly expert, but a very distinguished entomologist whose records are almost certainly reliable.

There are references to Herefordshire in Cynthia Longfield's *The Dragonflies of the British Isles*[1]. She includes Herefordshire in the list of localities for several of the common damselflies, but the only dragonfly listed for Herefordshire is the Club-tailed. All modern accounts of British Dragonflies list the Wye as one of the few British rivers to host the Club-tail, but there are no references to how far up stream it can be found, nor is there any comment made as to the density of the River Wye populations.

One strange record exists in these very limited historical Herefordshire Dragonfly records. John Henry Wood records Ruddy Darter from Devereux Park[2]. This is strange because Wood lived in the late 19th early 20th centuries when the Ruddy Darter was rare in Britain and only known from six southern English counties[3]. I discuss the significance of this record in my species account of the Downy Emerald!

Just one survey of Herefordshire Dragonflies had previously been conducted, but this only lasted one year and was the work of a lone recorder. David Parker carried out his survey in 1977 and stated that the weather in 1977 was "not ideal for the observation and recording of Odonata, there being many cloudy, cool and windy days."

In his introduction Parker went on to say that his survey was "very much a preliminary one and needs to be followed up in forthcoming seasons". Ten years later I did just that and yet after nearly 20 years there are still unvisited pools and

---

1 Wayside and Woodland Series – Warne (1937)
2 Woolhope Naturalists Field Club (1954)
3 Lucas W. 1900

other sites where recording has not been carried out at the right time of year, or where longer periods of observation are needed.

However, I believe that more recording would not have revealed more species for the county, it would just have filled in more of the blank spaces on the dot maps. More recorders might also have produced more records for migrant species such as Red-veined Darter, for which we have records from one site, and Yellow-winged Darter; both are occurring more and more regularly in the Midlands, and even breeding on occasions. With the range expansion that is occurring with some species I'm sure that in the future new colonists will arrive: Yellow-winged Darter might well be one of them, and following its rapid colonisation of the lower Avon in neighbouring Worcestershire, so might the Scarce Chaser.

• ● •

Irridescent sheen on the wings of a Migrant Hawker

Habitat

Ponds

*This fine pool (just south of Leominster) surrounded by Typha
was once part of the estate belonging to the house in the background*

Herefordshire is shaped like a saucer: the central lowland area, which is dominated by the valley of the River Wye and its main tributary the Lugg, is on Old Red Sandstone. This is overlain by well drained glacial deposits, sandy silts etc. The clay tends to concentrate in the river valleys and lower ground and may be augmented by alluvial clays on the river floodplains. The lower-lying parishes in the county support higher densities of ponds[1] because clay is more predominant and the water table is higher. For example Pembridge, Letton and Madley have relatively large numbers of ponds, reaching in excess of five ponds per square kilometre compared to the English average of 1.7. Such ponds are typically between 100 to 2500 square metres in area. Most of the smaller ponds were dug for the watering of stock and/or horses. In some areas ponds were formed after the digging of pits for clay which was used for daub, cooking pots, tiles and latterly for brick making. The smaller ponds, which periodically dry up, provide a good habitat for amphibians,

---

1 The map on page 33 showing species intensity indicates how the 10km squares with the largest numbers of species mostly follow the river valleys where there are the most ponds.

Herefordshire Dragonflies – All pools recorded

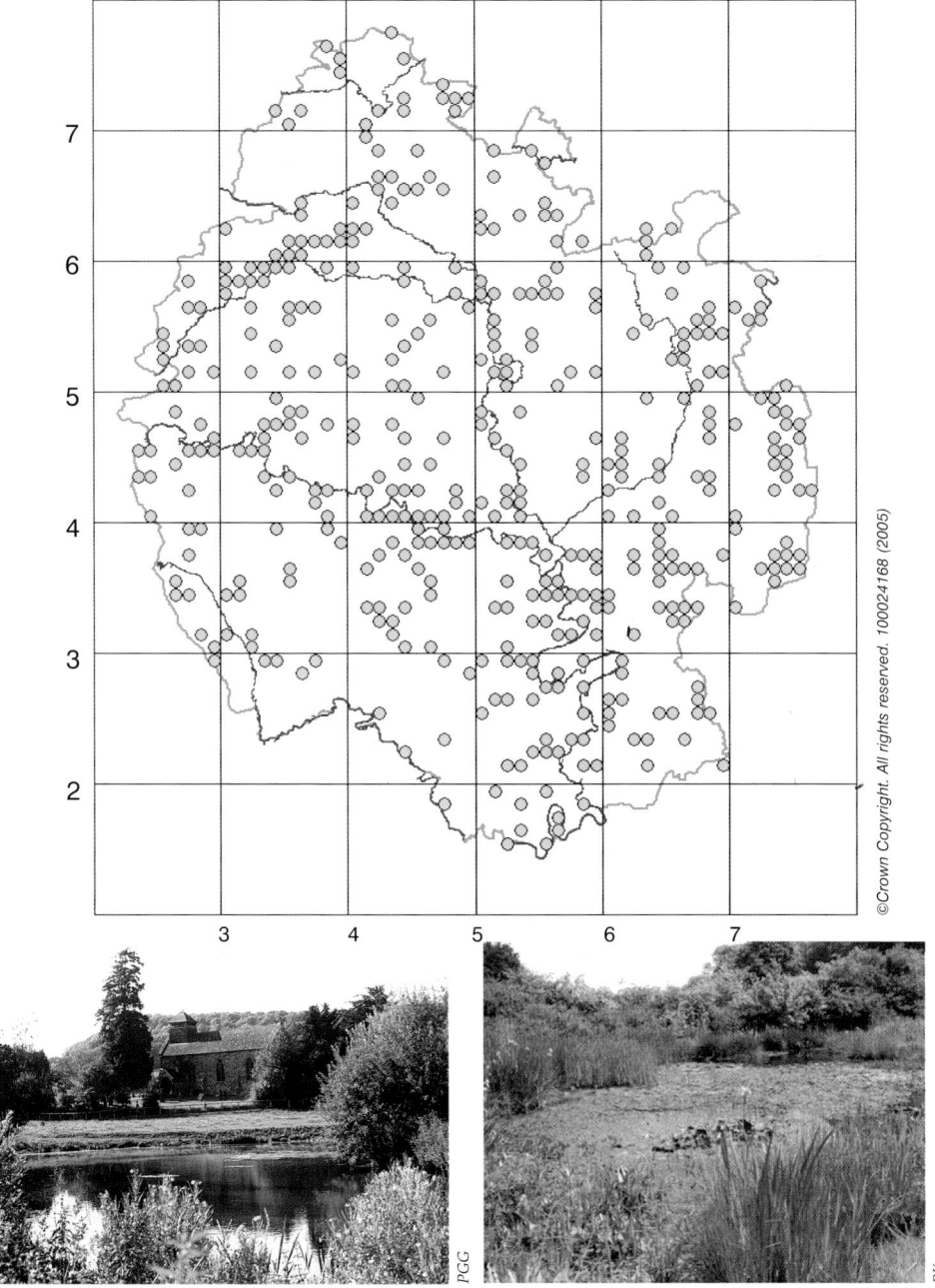

*A well-vegetated, unpolluted pool
with an open aspect at Brinsop*

*Woodlea Little Dewchurch,
created by Phyll and Richard King*

particularly for newts, but are much less suitable for dragonflies whose larvae cannot survive if a pool dries up completely. Other ponds have been deliberately constructed around farmsteads as horse, duck or fish ponds. These also are often unsuitable for dragonfly larvae because the water is not clear or clean enough. Where the ponds were located close to the buildings they would serve in emergencies as fire ponds.

On the higher ground in the northeast and south of the county the formations comprise sandstones and mudstones with a greater concentration of the harder sandstones. The ponds on the higher, steeper ground are often of larger construction because water may only hold once the water table is reached, requiring more extensive excavation. For example on the freer draining ground on the Bromyard plateau in Hatfield, Grendon Bishop and Bredenbury the majority of ponds are 2,500 to 5,000 square metres in area, many are stream or spring-fed. The average pond density on this formation is between 1 and 1.5 ponds per square kilometre.

Hard Silurian Limestone is to be found in several parts of the county. The three largest areas for this formation are the northwest Herefordshire Hills, the Woolhope Dome and the west flank of the Malvern Hills. These landscapes typically have low pond densities.

On the river terraces beside the River Wye kettle-holes were formed after the last ice age. As the ice retreated the hollows were filled with water creating a series of natural lakes and pools. Although often modified by 'restoration' several still exist to the south of the Wye between Hay and Hereford. The Lawn Pool at Moccas Park is one of the best known of these natural landscape features. Natural ponds and pools are particularly special because, apart from supporting rare or unusual freshwater life, they contain uninterrupted sequences of sediment with preserved pollen and wood deposits which can inform us about past climatic conditions and vegetation communities. They are also nationally scarce; it has been estimated that only 2% of all English ponds are of natural origin.

The county also has its fair share of moats with 120 confirmed sites. These were usually constructed for ornamental rather than defensive purposes. Lower Brockhampton near Bromyard is one of the finest examples of a moated medieval manor house in England. The moat here provides a sunny habitat for a healthy population of the commoner damselflies and dragonflies. However, most of the moat at Bronsil Castle, which is clearly a defensive feature, is too heavily shaded to host dragonflies.

Herefordshire is also renowned for its large country estates. Medieval moats, such as the one of the Court of Noke, were transformed into water features in the 17th century, but the great period of the country house was in the 18th and 19th centuries. On many of the larger estates at this period many ornamental lakes and pools were constructed. For example at Croft Castle (National Trust) a series of fish pools were constructed in what is now known as Fishpool Valley (SSSI), at Berrington Hall (National Trust) a pool with an island fed by a tributary of the River Lugg was created by Capability Brown and at Eastnor Castle (a private visitor attraction) a lake was constructed as backdrop to the castle in the 19th Century. Many of these ornamental lakes have been planted with waterlilies which are ideal habitat for the Red-eyed Damselfly, as is the case at Berrington.

In the mid 20th Century we began to lose ponds in Herefordshire. Some were filled in as pasture was converted into arable and others were destroyed because ponds no longer had an economic function within the modern farm economy, or were lost simply through neglect. It has been estimated that there was an overall loss of 30% of ponds within the county from the 1920s to the 1980s[4]. Most of these losses occurred in the fertile arable farmland of the central plain and mainly the smaller field ponds were affected.

---

4 Brian A. and Harding B. (1997)

PGG

Stretton Sugwas Gravel Pit soon after extraction ceased – ideal habitat for early colonists such as Black-tailed Skimmer and Common Blue Damselfly.

PGG

A perfect pool for many species of Dragonfly at Mathon old sandpit – sheltered, but sunny, and a good growth of submerged, floating and marginal vegetation.

In the latter half of the 20th Century new fishing pools were constructed across the county for both commercial and private amenity use. Even though fish, and carp in particular, feed upon dragonfly and damselfly larvae, many of these fishing pools provide excellent habitat for Dragonflies. They are invariably sunny because the banks are kept quite clear but hedges and sheltering trees are often a feature. Submerged and floating vegetation exists without the pool being allowed to become choked with excessive growth or algal-bloom and the jetties and trodden fishermen's pitches are attractive for some species, especially the Black-tailed Skimmer.

The extraction industry has left its mark in Herefordshire as it has over the rest of the country. Several gravel pits are associated with river valleys, as at Stretton Sugwas in the Wye Valley and Bodenham and Wellington in the Lugg Valley. Others exploited glacial deposits. At Mathon the sand and gravel was washed down into a lake which formed against the southern edge of the ice-cap which extended that far south in the last ice-age. Gravel pits quite quickly become less attractive dragonfly habitat once extraction ceases. The process of natural succession ensures optimum conditions during the first few years after the earth movers and diggers depart and then with maturity comes scrub followed by trees and resulting shade. However, this natural progression has been interrupted at several of Herefordshire's former gravel pits because the pools and lakes – the legacy of gravel extraction – are put to other uses: fishing at Mathon, recreation and conservation at Bodenham and probably at Stretton Sugwas in due course. Alternatively the land is returned to agriculture or silviculture, which, apart from one pool is the case at Aymestrey. As far as I know only at Wellington near Marden and at the Hereford Quarry on the Bromyard Road, is extraction currently taking place.

No account of Herefordshire's ponds would be complete without mentioning the many and varied garden ponds that seem to be more and more popular. Evidence of a marked increase can only be anecdotal but I am left in no doubt that there has been a very significant expansion in the number of these very valuable, mini nature reserves. As they are not marked on maps and by their very nature are hidden away on private land, they have been largely unsurveyed. If it had been possible to receive records from each one the distribution maps for species like the Broad-bodied Chaser, Southern Hawker, Large-red Damselfly and the commoner blue damselflies would be much more densely dotted.

Herefordshire Rivers and Canals

The River Wye runs through the centre of the county and all other rivers in Herefordshire except the Teme and Leadon drain into it. The Lugg, which is itself fed by the Arrow and the Frome, is its most significant tributary. The Lugg is barely more than a bubbling, stoney-bottomed brook when it enters the county at Stapleton just north of Presteigne. It then cuts its way through limestone gorges at Kinsham and Aymestrey before leaving the hills behind it at Mortimer's Cross, after which it flows across the lowland marls of the Old Red Sandstone in central Herefordshire (it has flowed over and through the rim and into the 'saucer'). It is a sedate and mature river that winds its way across the ancient lammas meadows near its confluence with the Wye at Mordiford.

The disproportionately wide floodplain of the Lugg across central Herefordshire indicates that it was once a much larger river. In fact, in pre-glacial times the Teme fed into the Lugg before it was diverted by ice to join the Severn, and the Wye was just another tributary of this 'super-Lugg'.

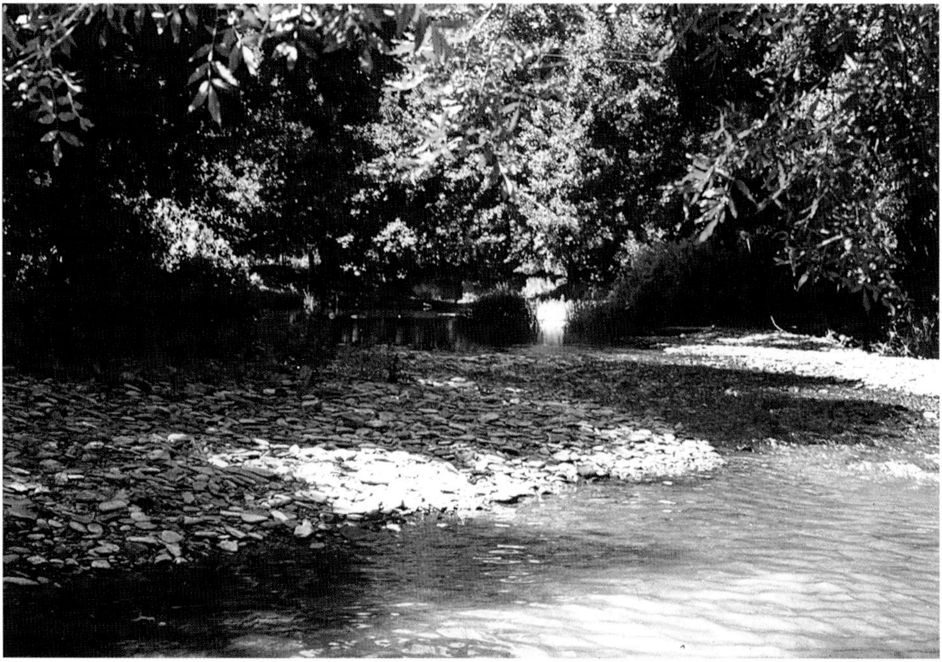

PGG

Mottled sunlight on the upper reaches of the Lugg, home for the Beautiful Demsoielle.

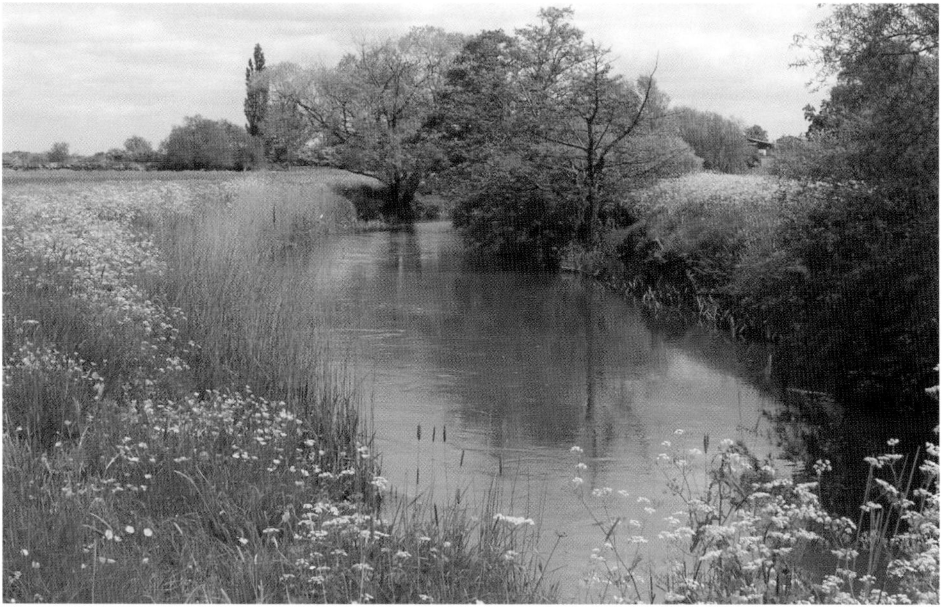

PGG

The Lugg as it crosses the Lugg Meadows, home to the Banded Demoiselle, White-legged Damselfly and the Club-tailed Dragonfly.

The enlarged floodplain of the lower Lugg explains the presence of the extensive meadows – Lugg Meadow itself and Hampton Meadow are both Herefordshire Nature Trust reserves and abound with Banded Demoiselles, White-legged Damselflies and also host the Club-tailed Dragonfly.

By the time the Wye enters Herefordshire at Hay it has lost much of the youthful character associated with an upland river, but although wide and meandering its flow is still interrupted by intermittent rushes through mini-rapids and round shingle-splits or islands. As the water level drops in summer quite extensive shingle beaches are exposed and lagoons form within the river-bed. Common and Ruddy Darters are attracted to these temporary pools and Black-tailed Skimmers find a false paradise on the shingle – false because they are enticed to the river-bed by the bare stony surfaces, and then lay eggs in the lagoons which stand no chance of surviving the inevitable swollen flood-waters that surge down the river later in the year.

The three dragonfly species that are completely at home in the waters of the Wye are the Banded Demoiselle, the White-legged Damselfly and the Club-tailed Dragonfly. Although the two damselflies populate all of the Wye in Herefordshire the Club-tail is not found upstream from Bredwardine. It prefers the fully mature river which flows with muddy bottom between steeper banks, highly vegetated by entangled Brambles, Nettles, Hogweeds, Balsam, Tansy Yellow-cress, Loosestrife, Reed Canary-grass, sedges and rushes – to name but a few. It shuns the stretches of bank shaded by willows that line many sections of the Wye's lowland course.

At Mordiford, just down stream from Hereford, the Wye is joined by the Lugg and the combined streams form extravagant loops around Ballingham Hill, King's Caple, How Caple and Foy; almost as if they are anxious to stay in Herefordshire as long as possible.

PGG

River Wye from the Seven Sisters Rocks – June 2005, with rafts of Water Crow-foot in flower.

When it winds its way south of Ross the Wye takes further evasive action with more huge detours round the towering wooded rocks at Symonds Yat and The Doward, finally slipping out of Herefordshire and joining forces with the Monnow at Monmouth.

The Arrow and the Frome are tributaries of the Lugg. They are not alike in character, but both host mixed populations of the Banded and Beautiful Demoiselles. The Arrow is quite wide, swift flowing, shallow, stoney-bottomed and shingly whereas the Frome is narrower, often shaded, sometime quite incised, well vegetated with a slower flow and a less stoney or shingly bed.

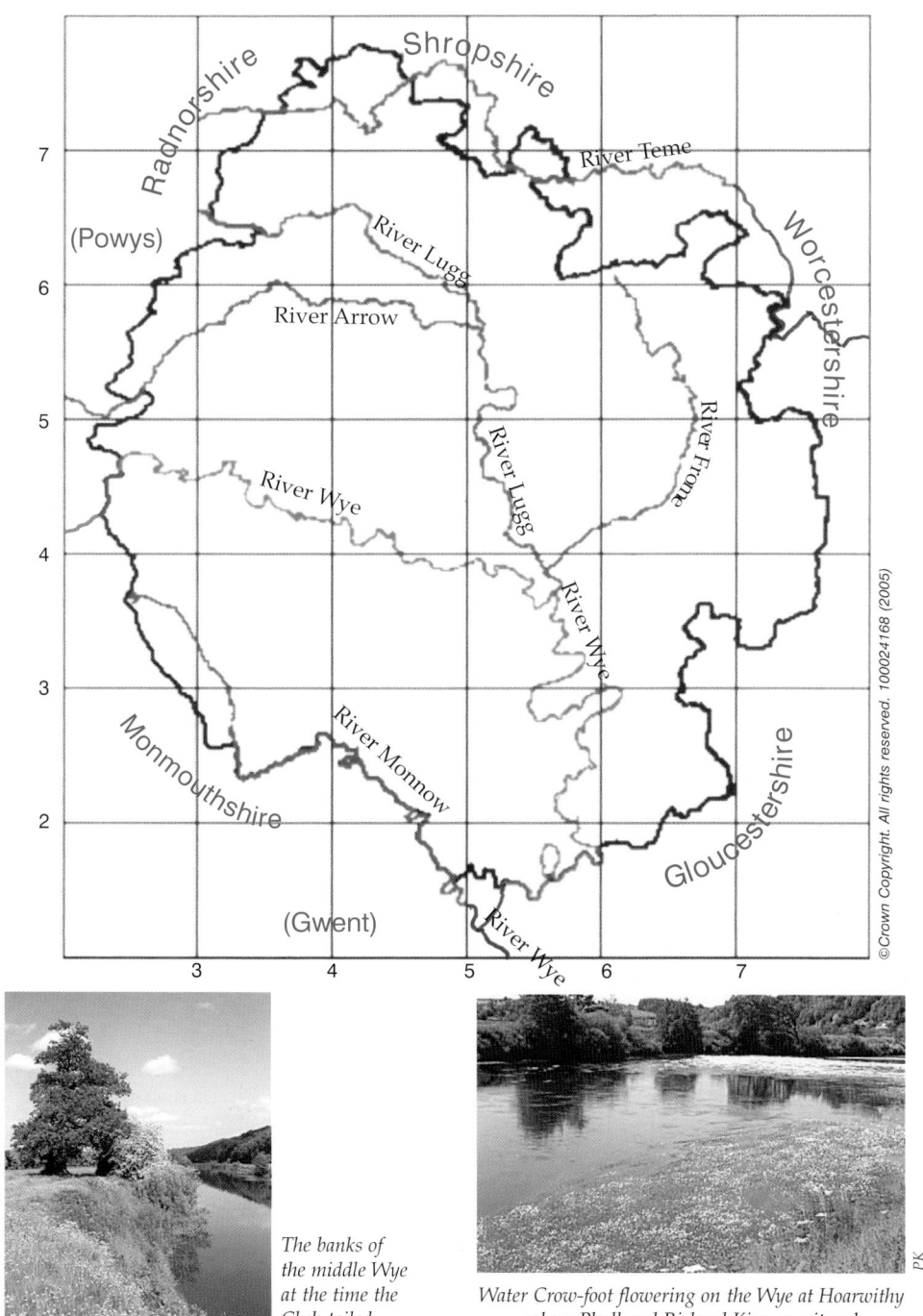

The banks of the middle Wye at the time the Club-tailed emerges.

Water Crow-foot flowering on the Wye at Hoarwithy where Phyll and Richard King monitored the emergence of Club-tailed Dragonflies.

PK

The Monnow forms the south western border of the county. It is fed by the Escley Brook, the Dulas Brook and the River Dore and forms a youthful upland river-system of rushing water tumbling over rocks and boulders, then around gravel and shingle-spits and stoney rapids further down stream. So much of this river system however is heavily shaded by stream-side Alders and consequently is unsuitable for any dragonfly species. On the few sunny stretches Beautiful Demoiselles and Large-red Damselflies can be found in May and June.

The Teme flirts with the county boundary in the north and north east of Herefordshire. This river and its tributary the Clun, which runs for just a couple of kilometres in Herefordshire, flows into the Severn. For most of its Herefordshire course it is an upland stream, providing ideal habitat for the Beautiful Demoiselle, but when it forms the eastern boundary of the parish of Whitbourne it has assumed a sedate lowland demeanour and is 'Banded Demoiselle territory' and hosts a healthy population of the Club-tailed Dragonfly.

In many parts of the country canals form an important habitat for dragonflies, but very few canals were built in Herefordshire, so it is not surprising they now comprise a habitat of very little consequence in the county. The Gloucester to Hereford Canal was completed in 1845, but was never a great success and now only retains water in a few isolated stretches. The best of these for dragonflies is at Monkhide (SO64) and to the north of Hereford city at Burcott (SO54). There is some water in the south near Munsely, but access is difficult and I failed to find a spot that wasn't too shaded for Dragonflies.

Also in the middle of the 19th century the Leominster Canal was started, but never finished – it reached as far as Tenbury. I have failed to find stretches of water along its former route, although I believe some exist.

PGG

The Hereford to Gloucester Canal at Monkhide.

The Natural History of Dragonflies

Steve Roe

In evolutionary terms dragonflies are very ancient creatures. Of the insects still largely unchanged today, only Bristletails (Silverfish) – 400 million years, Cockroaches – 250 million years and Mayflies preceded the Dragonflies. Two hundred million years ago, before the Age of the Dinosaurs, in the carboniferous period, when trees and flowers did not exist, when there were no birds or bees, butterflies or beetles and long before any mammals, dragonflies flew and hunted their prey[1].

Some of these dragonflies were massive with a wing span of almost a metre, but in every other way their body structures were the same as the dragonflies we know today. Without doubt, they are remarkably successful, and awe inspiring insects!

Damselflies are smaller and far daintier than dragonflies, much weaker fliers and less conspicuous, but often present in much greater concentrations. The family name is Zygoptera meaning 'equal wings' – the front and back wings are of equal size and shape. Dragonflies are Anisoptera meaning 'different wings' normally the hindwing of a dragonfly is broader than the forewing.

Dragonflies normally rest with their wings horizontal although there are always exceptions *(see The Club-tailed Dragonfly)*, and damselflies rest with their wings folded along their abdomen (except for the Emerald Damselfly).

Adult Behaviour

Both temperature and sunshine are essential for observing adult dragonflies. Strong winds will prevent flight, so select the day and conditions with care. In cooler or breezier conditions, however, dragonflies will "rest up" on floating vegetation or on bankside plants, at times such as this. Therefore, for the observer careful observations at the water margin can yield opportunities to study the animal at close hand whilst it is relatively immobile.

Dragonflies are carnivorous and feed 'on the wing', adeptly taking aerial prey such as midges, mayflies, moths and butterflies. Chaser and Club-tailed dragonflies will rest on a perch taking stock of prey and also of other individuals of their species in the vicinity. Different species occupy different niches at the water: temporally (period of time when on the wing), vertically and horizontally (along habitat). The best way in which to become familiar with these behaviours is to spend time observing. Species may patrol the open water (such as Hawkers), or spend periods motionless amongst vegetation (for example the Chasers). Species that do patrol the open water fly at quite different heights, and at different densities. One can watch a pool alive with hundreds of Coenagrion damselflies amongst the vegetation and on the waters surface, and yet only observe two or three of larger dragonflies such as the Southern Hawker patrolling the same area.

Males may hold territories, awaiting females. These territories may be agressively defended, with newly-arriving males confronted and usually chased away. Other species may occupy territory passively, or move territories often. This latter behaviour is quite characteristic of the damselflies who may hold and defend territories that change rapidly.

---

1 Simon H. (1972)

Migrant Hawkers incop the 'wheel' position or 'heart' position.

An Emerald-Damselfly pair inserting eggs into a stem of Water-horsetail. They continued to descend the stem until the female was completely submerged, she remained under water for 10 minutes.

Common Blue Damselfy in the 'wheel' or 'heart' position

Mating behaviour

Mating behaviour is variable between the species. All species will adopt the "wheel position" (perhaps more appropriately referred to in France as "le coeur" – the heart) in which the male takes hold of the female behind the head using his anal clasping appendages, and if amenable she will curl her abdomen around under him so as to connect with his secondary (accessory) genitalia located under the second and third abdominal segment. Following mating, the female may remain accompanied – in tandem - as she oviposits (lays eggs), or she may oviposit alone. If this is so, the male may or may not remain in residence as a "guard". Eggs of some species may be laid by insertion into the stems or leaves of aquatic or even bank-side plants (eggs tend to be elongated or oval), or for other species they may be simply flicked off the abdomen into water, mud or dead plant materials (eggs tend to be spherical). Eggs generally are laid in large numbers, hatching between 2 and 4 weeks. Eggs of some species – such as Lestes or Aeshna – enter a diapause to hatch early next season after the intervening winter.

Let me recount two observed examples of ovipositing: the Large Red Damselfly male was retaining a hold on the female, lowering her into position over suitable plants into which she laid eggs with a specialised blade-like spike *(see picture top right page 22)*. The ovipositor allows eggs to be deposited into the plant stem directly. The female may be lowered under the water's surface in order to oviposit, before her mate pulls her out to move onto a new egg-laying site: secondly, I observed a female Broad-bodied Chaser ovipositing by skimming 5cm over favourable areas of water at a large pond, dipping her abdomen into the water, overlooked by a hovering male. Her activity was only broken by the same male clashing with her and mating again, before allowing her to return to her duties. This act was played out for about forty minutes as I observed; it left me exhausted ! Her eggs are coated in a gelatinous substance which protect them from temperature extremes and predation, allowing them to adhere to plant material or the substrate.

Larval Development

For the casual dragonfly observer, the colourful adult phase is all that is often observed. Yet these animals spend the vast majority of their lives underwater as larvae, and the study of larvae is actually straight-forward, although care should be taken not to cause them any harm. With some experience mature larvae may be identified in the net or sorting tray. Damselfly larvae possess external gills in the form of three feather-like structures called caudal lamellae located at the tip of the abdomen. Dragonfly larvae possess internal gills and their abdomen lacks such feather-like structures. Much preferable to the study of live larvae is the collection of exuviae – the cast final skin after emergence. The exuvia contains

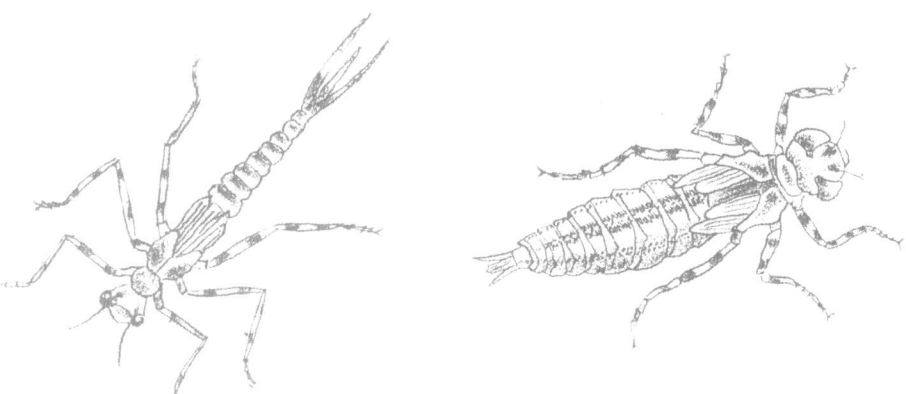

all the diagnostic features required for a species to be identified at home under the microscope, and their collection does not harm the emerged adult. Indeed exuvia collection is a method of confirming successful breeding for the species at a site .

Successive stages – known as stadia – occur as the animal develops. There are usually between ten and fifteen stadia. The time between hatching and emergence from the water may take anything from one to four years depending on the species, the availability of prey and the temperature. Blue-tailed Damselfly may complete a single generation within a year in the north of it's range, and yet towards the south of it's range (in southern Europe) it may complete three generations within one year alone . It has been shown that the Scarce Blue-tailed Damselfly can develop in Britain within one year. In a manner similar to many other invertebrates, the animal splits its skin, emerges and enlarges before it's chitinous skin hardens again. As larvae develop they increase morphological characteristics of the adult form, although the development of key features (such as abdominal spines and leaf scales) tend to occur primarily during the later stadia towards the end of the larval phase before emergence. Moulting also allows the regeneration of body parts (such as legs or external gills) that may have been lost to predators.

Odonata larvae appear to be tolerant of acidity although the pH will affect the plant communities at a site and therefore the ovipositing opportunities and plant architecture available to the larvae; some species have shown a preference for certain plant species.

Larval Behaviour

When hunting larvae remain immobile, seeking to capture and overwhelm prey by ambush strategies. This behaviour can be readily observed in the collecting tray along with some water and vegetation or substrate from the site. Larve occupy distinct aquatic habitats according to species. Some species – such as Emeralds, Skimmers or Chasers possess hairy bodies which to trap particles of dirt so as to camouflage them, and such species tend to dwell at the bottom of the water body. Visibility is poor there and so such species tend to have better developed antennae for 'feeling' their prey (and correspondingly they have smaller eyes). By contrast, other species dwell within vegetation much nearer the surface. Hawker larvae live amongst the plants in the clearer waters nearer to the surface and have larger eyes. These larvae tend to be more elongated in profile: a more streamlined body is better suited to rapid movement when required. Indeed dragonfly larvae can project a jet of water from their gills (located in their rectum) enabling a rapid movement for evasion of predators or to assist in the capture of prey.

Predation

Dragonflies possess a 'labial mask', which is unique to this group of invertebrates. This mask is either covering part of the face, or is located under the head, and it's shape and structure is important for identification. The labial mask is the main weapon of the Dragonfly, functioning rather like a articulated trident. Once a prey is located and in range, the labium unfolds rapidly and catches the prey with its gripping parts, spines and armatures . The labium then recoils back to the head, allowing the mouthparts to consume the prey. If this strike is not at first successful, the speed of the action means that a

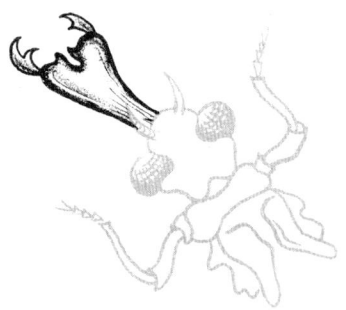

Dragonfly larva with labiam extended

number of strikes might be attempted. Dragonfly larvae take small aquatic invertebrates, small fish, tadpoles and each other. Damselfly larvae take micro-invertebrates. Research has revealed that larvae are not selective feeders: they take what they can manage and what is available. Larger larvae will feed on both large and small prey, and they react to prey size and its movement.

Larvae are preyed upon by other odonata larvae, fish and larger aquatic invertebrates. At a garden pond in Stoke Bliss Pond snails were observed eating a Southern Hawker larva.

Emergence

When conditions are right for emergence, the larva will leave the water for its adult future. Indeed, it has to leave once its metabolism has reacted to correct conditions. This is because the gills cease to function, the labial mask becomes disconnected: it cannot breathe or feed. For some species (Emerald Damselfly, Hawkers and Darters) emergence occurs following a pause in development (known as diapause), prompting a synchronised emergence of all mature larvae of the species within a period of days or in some cases hours. For other species the emergence will occur over a longer period of time, with some species beginning earlier in the year than others. Typically emergence will start with the Large Red Damselfly in April and continue until the Common Darter or Migrant Hawker emerge in August or even occasionally September.

The larvae will emerge from the water onto a suitable stem or bankside surface. I have watched larvae crossing muddy edges of a pond to climb up onto grasses or reeds a metre or more from the waters edge. It is, of course, not uncommon at high densities for many individuals to emerge on the same favourable stem of vegetation, and successive larvae may be observed clinging onto old exuviae clustered at key points on this emergence stem.

Once a suitable support has been gained, the larvae remains there for sometime as it emerges. A weak point behind the head allows the adult to break out from its larval skin. It remains partially emerged for some time as it's legs and head parts harden. Once this is

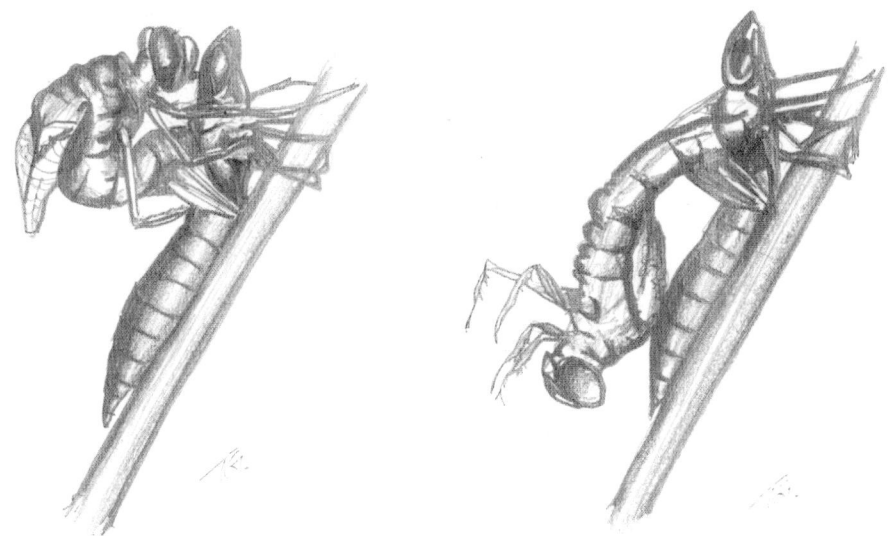

An adult Southern Hawker breaks out of its larval skin.

LC

Southern Hawker recently emerged from nearby exuvia.

LC

Broad-bodied Chaser recently emerged from nearby exuvia.

PGG

A badly deformed Southern Hawker.

completed, the adult can extract its abdomen from the skin, allowing the abdomen to extend and fill out with fluid before hardening. During this process the wings slowly expand and fill with fluid before hardening. The emergence period is a time of danger for the adult as it is largely defenceless, unable to fly and with a soft body. During emergence dragonflies can be attacked by ants, birds, spiders etc. Some species will begin their emergence under cover of darkness so as to avoid predation. Furthermore, if the dragonfly has selected a poor emergence site, then wings can be damaged if they have insufficient room to expand or if they can readily be snagged on twigs or other obstructions. I have seen a Southern Hawker with a damaged wing as a result of emerging too close to thistles. For the observer, emergence is a fascinating process and an opportunity for a detailed examination close at hand. Initially the dragonfly lacks colouration and is referred to as a teneral in it's first few hours.

After emergence the dragonfly has a period of time away from the water in which it matures. This distance varies considerably with dragonfly species dispersing further away than damselfly species. Common Blue Damselflies may only disperse a few metres into adjacent vegetation or habitat, but by contrast one may see hawker dragonflies along hedgerows or woodland tracks and in gardens miles away from any water. After spending this time away from water to reach maturity, mature adults will then return to water to breed. They may return to their emergence site, or disperse to other waterbodies.

Mortality

Damselflies may only live for a short period of time as adults: perhaps 15 or 20 days. Some may live longer if they have good conditions, plentiful prey and perhaps lack of

Emerald Damselfly trapped in a web, framed in the flowering head of a club-rush

competition from other Dragonflies. An Emperor has been recorded with a life-span including the maturation and reproductive stages of 60 days! The capture then re-capture of marked individuals has revealed 40-50 day life-span on several occasions, and a record of 69 days which was held by an Emerald Damselfly[1]. It can be territorial clashes or over amorous mating activities which injure or kill a dragonfly. They can also be preyed on by birds, frogs and by other dragonflies. Roger Maskew observed a great-crested Newt eating an ovipositing Southern Hawker which then attempted to fly about with half of its abdomen missing. They have recently been reported to be attacked by hornets. Damselflies being smaller can also be taken by pond-dwelling insects (such as Pond Skaters and Water Boatmen) whilst mating or ovipositing. Emergence can be a particularly damaging time; I am constantly surprised during my searches for exuviae how many dead or dying individuals I find trapped in spiders webs, or having failed to emerge successfully with twisted abdomens and damaged wings.

In this chapter an attempt has been made to describe the basic life history of British odonata. Where the reader feels a need of more detailed information there are many excellent texts are available.

Banded Demoiselle caught in a spider web

1   Corbet P.S. 1962

Glossary

Anal appendages – *see page 30* – sometimes referred to as 'claspers' – male dragonflies use them to grasp the female round the head or pronotum during mating.

Antehumeral stripes – a pair of light coloured stripes along the top of (or at the front of) the thorax. Sometimes referred to as shoulder stripes or thoracic stripes. Not present in all species.

Costa – the vein which forms the leading edge of front of each wing.

Exuvia – the shed larval skin.

Frons – *see page 30*. The upper front part of the head – the forehead.

Ovipositing – egg laying.

Pronotum – the shield like plate which covers the front of the thorax.

Pruinescence – a grey/blue powdery looking covering which develops on the abdomen of maturing dragonflies – specially chasers and darters.

Pterostigma – *see page 30*. A dark or coloured patch on the outer region of the leading wing edge. NB. The **False-pterostigma** in the demoiselles is positioned in the same part of the wing but is white. Sometimes referred to as a pseudo-pterostigma.

Tandem or "in tandem" – when the male has clasped the female by the back of the head and the pair are so joined. Sometimes referred to as "in-cop".

Teneral – a newly emerged adult dragonfly before it has acquired full colour.

LC

The compound eyes of a Damselfly.

Anatomy

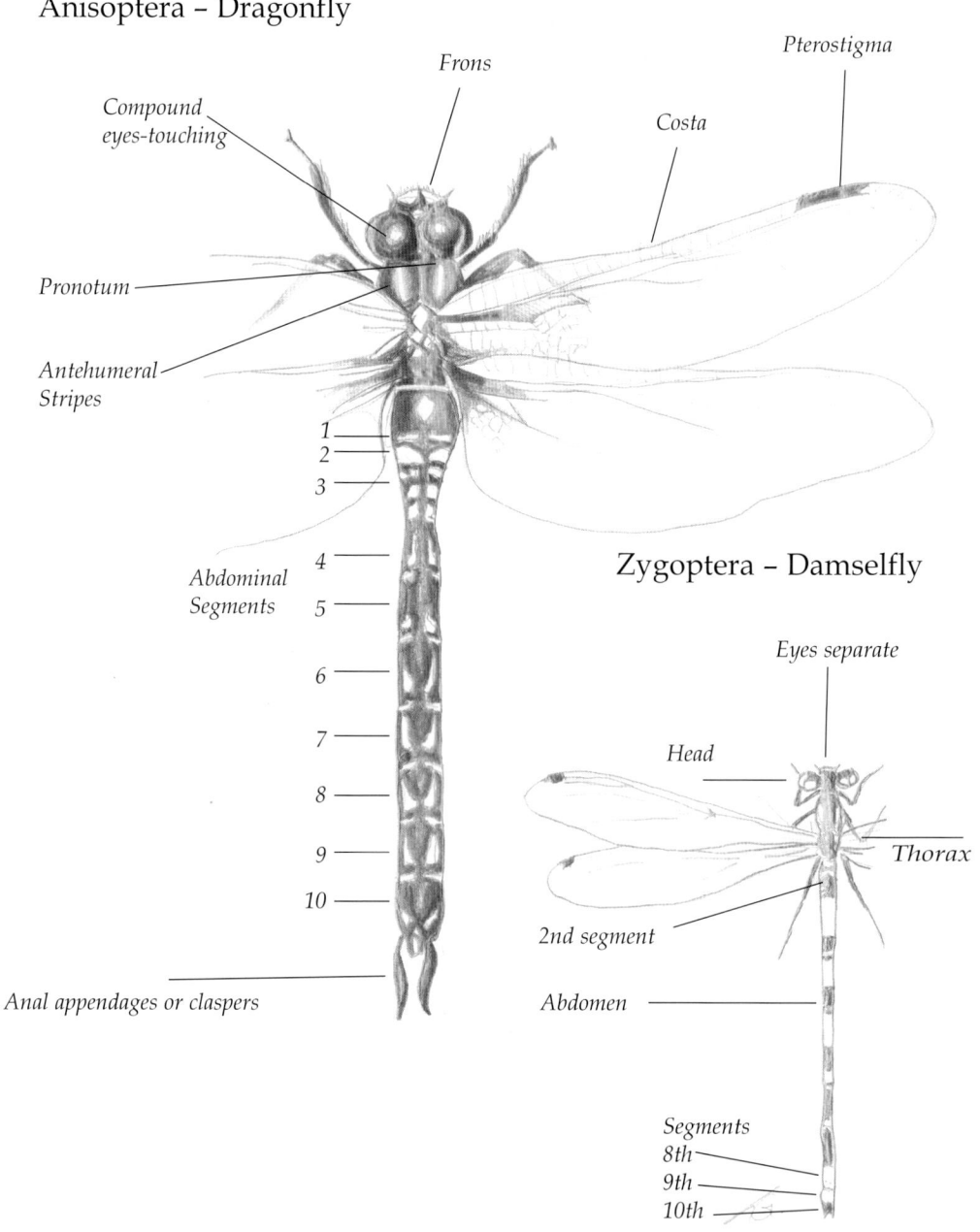

Anisoptera – Dragonfly

Frons

Pterostigma

Compound
eyes-touching

Costa

Pronotum

Antehumeral
Stripes

1
2
3

Abdominal
Segments

4
5
6
7
8
9
10

Anal appendages or claspers

Zygoptera – Damselfly

Eyes separate

Head

Thorax

2nd segment

Abdomen

Segments
8th
9th
10th

CHECKLIST

British Breeding Species
The sequence and scientific nomenclature follows Askew (1988)

Herefordshire Species in bold
The numbers indicate breeding status (see key at the end of the list)

Damselflies – Zygoptera

Beautiful Demoiselle	*Calopteryx virgo*	2
Banded Demoiselle	*Calopteryx splendens*	1
Emerald Damselfly	*Lestes sponsa*	2
Scarce Emerald Damselfly	*Lestes dryas*	
White-legged Damselfly	*Platycnemis pennipes*	1
Large Red Damselfly	*Pyrrhosoma nymphula*	1
Red-eyed Damselfly	*Erythromma najas*	1
Small Red-eyed Damselfly	*Erythromma viridulum*	
Southern Damselfly	*Coenagrion mercuriale*	
Northern Damselfly	*Coenagrion hastulatum*	
Irish Damselfly	*Coenagrion lunulatum*	
Azure Damselfly	*Coenagrion puella*	1
Variable Damselfly	*Coenagrion pulchellum*	5
Common Blue Damselfly	*Enallagma cyathigerum*	1
Scarce Blue-tailed Damselfly	*Ischnura pumilio*	1
Blue-tailed Damselfly	*Ischnura elegans*	1
Small Red Damselfly	*Ceriagrion tenellum*	

Dragonflies – Anisoptera

Azure Hawker	*Aeshna caerulea*	
Common Hawker	*Aeshna juncea*	5
Migrant Hawker	*Aeshna mixta*	1
Southern Hawker	*Aeshna cyanea*	1
Brown Hawker	*Aeshna grandis*	3
Norfolk Hawker	*Aeshna isosceles*	
Emperor Dragonfly	*Anax imperator*	1
Lesser Emperor	*Anax parthenope*	
Hairy Dragonfly	*Brachytron pratense*	6
Club-tailed Dragonfly	*Gomphus vulgatissimus*	1
Golden-ringed Dragonfly	*Cordulegaster boltonii*	4
Downy Emerald	*Cordulia aenea*	3

Brilliant Emerald	*Somatochlora metallica*	
Northern Emerald	*Somotochlora arctica*	
Four-spotted Chaser	***Libellula quadrimaculata***	**4**
Scarce Chaser	*Libellula fulva*	
Broad-bodied Chaser	***Libellula depressa***	**1**
Black-tailed Skimmer	***Orthetrum cancellatum***	**1**
Keeled Skimmer	*Orthetrum coerulescens*	
Common Darter	***Sympetrum striolatum***	**1**
Highland Darter	*Sympetrum nigrescens*	
Red-veined Darter	***Sympetrum fonscolombii***	**6**
Yellow-winged Darter	*Sympetrum flaveolum*	
Ruddy Darter	***Sympetrum sanguineum***	**1**
Black Darter	***Sympetrum danae***	**5**
White-faced Darter	*Leucorrhinia dubia*	

KEY

Absolute proof of breeding	1
So abundant year after year that breeding can be assumed without doubt	2
Breeding – almost certain	3
Breeding probable	4
Breeding possible	5
Assumed not to be breeding	6

Breeding

Strict guidelines have been drawn up by the BDS as to what evidence is required as proof of breeding[1] and this is, a presence of exuvia or teneral insects. In this account I have simply described what I have seen, and for the most part this has been the adult insect. As a consequence there is inadequate proof of breeding for several Herefordshire species. Steve Roe, while carrying out a research project on Dragonfly larva, made confirmed breeding records for a number of sites in the county.

I have found exuvia at many ponds, but can only identify these with certainty for a limited number of species!

However breeding can be considered likely when several of the same species occur at the same site repeatedly over a period of years, or if they are observed 'in cop' (especially if there are several pairs). If they are observed ovipositing one can, at least, bestow upon the site the status of "attempted breeding".

---

1 Moore N.W. and Corbet PS (1990) and Prendergast E.D.V. (1997)

Herefordshire Dragonfly Species Intensity
(number of species per 10km²)

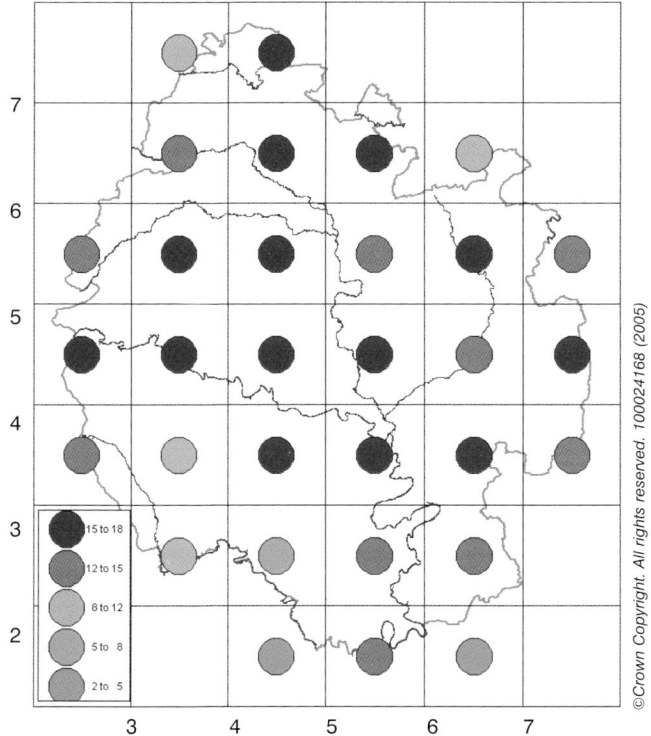

The Species Accounts

Flight Period – These sections are based on Herefordshire observations and very likely will differ from other counties.

Status – After 'Status-Herefordshire' there is a figure over 30. This is the number of 10 kilometre squares (hectads) in which the species has been recorded. There are records from 30 hectads but some only include a small area which is in Herefordshire.
This fraction of thirty acts as a **rarity indicator.**

Terminology – When "Dragonfly" is written with a capital letter it refers to dragonflies and damselflies as a general term. Dragonflies belong to the insect order ODONATA, but this term has not been used in the hope that the book will appeal to a wider audience if scientific language is kept to a minimum.

Photographs – All photograhs have been taken in Herefordshire; where the Dragonfly is rare in the county and no-one has been able to photograph it, I have not sought one from elsewhere.

The Damselflies *Zygoptera*

The two Demoiselles are classified as *Zygoptera*, but I have described them separately in this book.

Of the nine Herefordshire damselflies, the males of seven are blue (or strictly speaking, dark with blue markings), one is predominantly red and the other green. Two are very rare in Herefordshire and uncommon nationally: The Scarce Bluetail Damselfly and The Variable Damselfly. All are probably breeding but there is very little information about the Variable Damselfly and certainly no recorded evidence of breeding.

Only the White-legged Damselfly is a riverine species, but several of the more common damselflies frequently occur in good numbers beside rivers large and small. The Large Red Damselfly is a faithful companion of The Beautiful Demoiselle on the minor water-courses and as ubiquitous beside the major rivers.

Male and female damselflies of the same species vary in pattern and colouring. The females of many of the blue damselflies have green patterning and some are almost uniformly dark with virtually no pattern at all. It is much easier to identify males than females. Male and female damselflies are often seen flying or ovipositing in tandem. This is when the male grasps his partner behind her head with his anal claspers, both before and after mating *[see section on Natural History of Dragonflies]*.

The male needs bright markings to help it attract a female and defend its territory. The female, however, benefits from being as inconspicuous as possible when resting in waterside vegetation and when hunting away from water, which is something the males are much less likely to do.

As with many insects that occur in very large numbers, damselflies are victims of many types of prey. Birds, dragonflies, spiders, fish and even pond-snails are all damselfly predators. I have, on several occasions observed fish take ovipositing damselflies from below. When a damselfly has landed on the water surface I have watched it struggle towards the side or the sanctuary of a water-lily leaf, desperately trying to lift its wings, trapped by the surface tension, only to be sucked down into a probing fish mouth.

However the most evident predator is the pool-side spider. Occasionally dragonflies are caught in webs, but the sight of a distorted damselfly corpse suspended between stems of water plants is very common *(see pictures at the end of the 'Natural History' chapter pages 27 and 28)*. It often provides one with an excellent opportunity to study the damselfly in detail through a magnifying glass.

I very much doubt if any research has been carried out to identify spider species most likely to prey on Dragonflies, but I was able to have my identification of the spider *Larinioides cornutus* confirmed by Wayne Rixom (The Herefordshire Spider Recorder). *L. cornutus* caught and ate a Large Red Damselfly at a pool near to Little Marcle (SO63) – 28th May 1998.

Damselflies are, of course, predators themselves. On one occasion I witnessed Dr Michael Harper (The Moth Recorder for Herefordshire) record a new micro moth for the lake at Holme Lacey House (SO53) when he caught a Blue-tailed Damselfly in his net and then removed a tiny moth from the damselfly's mandibles, it was on the 7th August 1995 and the moth was *Bryotropha senectella*.

The Demoiselles *Calopteryx sp.*

These two spectacular looking species are larger than any other damselfly. With their shining metallic green, blue and bronze bodies and densely coloured wings, they have a tropical appearance which is enhanced by their dancing, butterfly-like flight. In Ireland they are called 'Jewelwing' - a wonderfully evocative name!

The males are easily separated: the Banded Demoiselle, as its name indicates, has it's wing colour concentrated in a dark blue blotch or band on the outer half of each wing, whereas the wings of the Beautiful Demoiselle are consistently clouded from base to tip.

In common with all other damselfly species, the females of both demoiselles are less conspicuous. This is because they spend much of their time perched on waterside vegetation hoping not to attract the attention of predators, rather than displaying themselves to catch a mate or defend a territory, which is the role of the more showy male.

It is much more difficult to tell the two females apart than it is the males. In both species the wings are uniformly tinted green, but the broader wings of the Beautiful Demoiselle have a slightly more orange/brown appearance. However, there is a more precise, more detailed way to separate the two species. Only the females of the two demoiselles have a white false pterostigma (the white marked cell towards the tip on the leading edge of each wing). In the Beautiful Demoiselle the false (or psuedo) pterostigma is approximately the same size on the fore and hind wings, but in the Banded Demoiselle it is twice as large on the fore wing as on the hind wing. A detail, but one which can be easily observed when the insect is at rest and an invaluable identification aid on the rare occasion when a female is present without a male to aid identification.

The two demoiselles do not commonly associate but there are always exceptions to every rule and on some of the smaller rivers (especially close to the confluence of small tributary and a larger river, both Beautiful Demoiselle and Banded Demoiselle species can be found together.

The lower reaches of the Lugg where it flows more slowly are the domain of the Banded Demoiselle, whereas the upper, faster flowing stretches of the Lugg host only the Beautiful Demoiselle. For about 2 miles upstream, however from the point where the Arrow joins the Lugg, the two species overlap. Along this stretch I noticed concentrations of Beautiful Demoiselle where the river runs faster. One theory is that these are sites of former water mills – a subject for more research!

The two demoiselles can also be found for most of the course of the Arrow in Herefordshire, but, except close to its confluence with the Lugg, Beautiful Demoiselle is more plentiful. They can also both be found co-existing on the lower reaches of the River Frome.

Wing waving and raised abdomen indicates the female Banded Demoiselles are receptive to a mate.

The Beautiful Demoiselle *Calopteryx virgo*

Beautiful Demoiselle – male

Beautiful Demoiselle – female

Flight Period

The Beautiful Demoiselle is on the wing from mid-May to early August, but is most abundant in June and July.

Status

National
Common in Wales and southwest England, the Lake District and southern Ireland. Almost absent from eastern England, mainly due to lack of suitable habitat.

Herefordshire – 21/30
Common in the right habitat, almost completely absent from the 'Wye corridor'. The full list of rivers, streams and brooks where the Beautiful Demoiselle has been recorded:

Cradley Brook	SO74	River Dore	SO33
Sapey Brook	SO75	River Monnow	SO43/42/41
Paradise Brook	SO75	Dulas Brook	SO32
River Leadon	SO73	Newbridge Brook	SO35
River Frome *(see map of miners)*		Jay Brook	SO37
Stony Brook	SO64	River Clun	SO37
Garren Brook	SO51	River Lugg	*(see map of rivers)*
Cage Brook	SO43	River Teme	*(see map of rivers)*
Back Brook	SO25	River Lodon	SO64
River Arrow	*(see map of rivers)*	Curl Brook	SO35

Beautiful Demoiselle
Calopteryx virgo

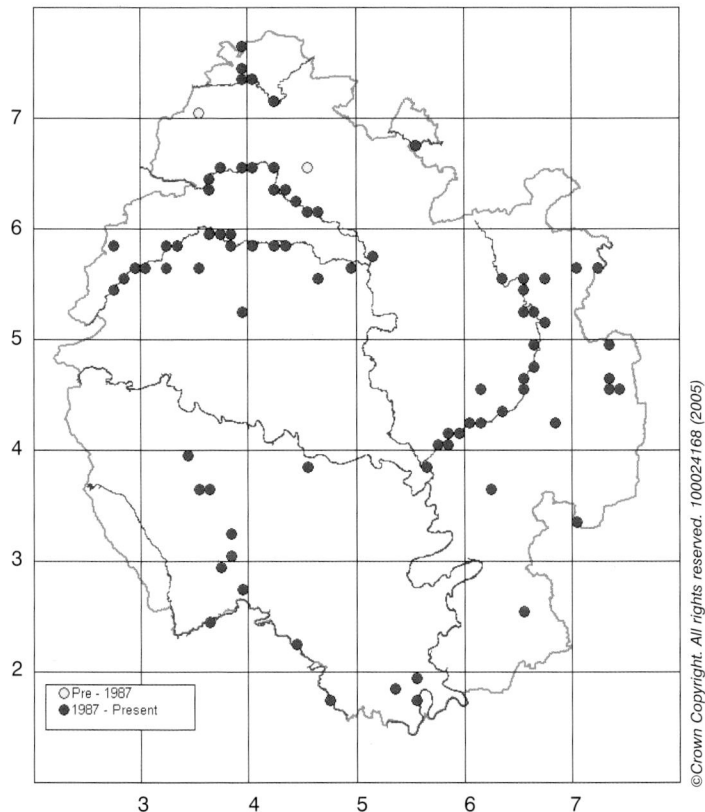

Legend:
- ○ Pre - 1987
- ● 1987 - Present

Habitat

The Beautiful Demoiselle favours unpolluted, moderate to fast flowing streams with gravely or stony bottoms, sometimes (notably River Frome) with a silted riverbed. Many otherwise suitable streams in Herefordshire such as long stretches of the Olchon and Escley Brooks and the River Dore are rendered unsuitable by heavy shading from streamside Alders. However, the Beautiful Demoiselle will tolerate more shade than the Banded Demoiselle, and seems to favour 'pools' of sunlight above the water surface or on bankside vegetation. The recent riverside felling beside the Escley Brook under a countryside stewardship scheme will allow the Beautiful Demoiselle to colonise this stream, which, with a more open aspect, will comprise a perfect habitat.

In May and June Beautiful Demoiselles and Large Red Damselflies are common associates and where they occur they are invariably the only Dragonfly species present. This is partially because of the time of year, but more significantly as a result of the habitat. In the east of the county, where invariably only small numbers of each species are present, there are small brooks, often heavily silted, with steep well vegetated sides, and because of the widespread and extensive nature of this habitat[1] the recording at sites has been more

PCG

Beautiful Demoiselle male with the sun
behind the observer shining onto the Demoiselle.

PCG

Beautiful Demoiselle male
between the observer and the sun.

representative than comprehensive. In the west of the County the same two species are more commonly encountered in greater numbers on wider, stony bottomed, faster flowing streams or rivers[2].

Description

The body of the male is metallic blue/green and the wings vary from a rich chocolate brown, through an even darker brown which appears almost black, to an intensely dark colour which contains shades of indigo. They darken with age and then the brown is more often seen as indigo. Their bodies and wings vary in colour depending on the way the light falls upon them. If you stand with sunlight shining from behind you onto this wonderful insect, the body is a shining dark green and the wings are almost black, but if the Beautiful Demoiselle is between you and the sun its body reflects a deep inky blue and the wings are brown *(see above)*.

The female has a metallic green-bronze body with the bronze normally confined to the last three segments of the abdomen, but with ageing it can be more extensive. The wings are very lightly tinted green-brown.

Behaviour

Single males establish small territories, which typically might amount to two or three metres of stream. They will sometimes patrol and chase off intruders. At other times they will settle on a prominent perch in the sunlight and intruders will be threatened by an upward flick of the hind wings. Both sexes, when perched on bankside vegetation, frequently raise their abdomen to a near-vertical position *(see bottom of next page)* which is the precursor to more wing flicking, or perhaps more accurately wing waving, which appears to indicate a willingness to mate.

The Beautiful Demoiselle is far less aggressively territorial than the Banded Demoiselle. It is not unusual to observe a party of four or five non-territorial males fluttering in the same

1 eg Honeylake Brook (Alleymoor) (SO4655). Stony Brook (Bosbury) (SO6843).
   Cradley Brook (Mathon) (SO7345)
2 R. Monnow (Cockshoot Wd) (SO4427). R. Dove (Pontrilas) (SO3927). R. Arrow (Hunton Br.) (SO3358)

pool of sunlight and perching communally. The pools of sunlight formed by gaps in streamside trees change with the passage of the day: thus the territories of the Beautiful Demoiselles are transitory, which might explain why it's territorial behaviour is relatively passive. By comparison, the Banded Demoiselle can 'dance' over the same patch of Water-crowfoot all day in constant sunshine.

On 1st June 2000 I was beside the River Arrow as far west as Kington. This was "real Beautiful Demoiselle territory". The river was fast flowing with a shingle bottom, but it was quite wide and it was passing through open pasture land. It was a gloriously sunny day, so I was surprised to find relatively low numbers of demoiselles. Then I came across a male Banded Demoiselle on a patch of Hemlock Water-dropwort and it was refusing to let a male Beautiful Demoiselle join it or even settle anywhere nearby. When I returned twenty minutes later they were still scrapping! However, on the same day a few miles downstream at Arrow Green Bridge beside a little, reedy backwater from the main river (where Beautiful Demoiselles were plentiful) there were several of both species co-existing with no apparent interaction.

Beautiful Demoiselles wander far less frequently from their preferred habitat than The Banded Demoiselle, but on 6th June 2003 Rob Havard, a conservationist working for the Herefordshire Nature Trust, saw as many as 20 in an old orchard at Newtown (SO617453). It is most likely that they originated from the River Lodon – half a kilometre to the East.

PGG

A female Beautiful Demoiselle with abdomen raised perpendicularly indicated her willingness to mate.

The Banded Demoiselle *Calopteryx splendens*

Male Banded Demoiselle eating a mayfly

Banded Demoiselle – female

Flight Period
Emergence starts in mid-May and it is on the wing until mid-August.

Status

National
Banded Demoiselles can be found in most of England. However, there are only a few isolated populations in the far north that reach up as far as the Scottish borders. They are common in the right habitat throughout most of Ireland.

Herefordshire – 27/30
They are plentiful throughout the course of The Wye in Herefordshire and on The Lugg from north of Leominster downstream to its confluence with the Wye. It also occurs in smaller numbers on many other water courses: River Monnow, River Frome, River Teme and River Arrow all host Banded Demoiselles at certain points along their course.

Habitat
Beautiful Demoiselles inhabit unpolluted, relatively slow flowing rivers and streams; normally with muddy bottoms. Most have open bank-side vegetation with limited shading from river-side trees. The full length of the Wye through Herefordshire is ideal habitat for the Banded Demoiselle. Many of the smaller tributaries (1 or 2 metres in width) also attract significant populations of Banded Demoiselles, but they all have silted/muddy bottoms, an open sunny aspect and a slow even flow of water.

Banded Demoiselles appear to be strongly attracted to the extensive beds of Water Crowfoot that are a feature of the Herefordshire Wye. Although the Banded Demoiselle could only be described as a riverine species it does occur on ponds and lakes far from a suitable river. On large lakes especially where there are islands, such as Berrington Pool (SO56), channels exist which resemble rivers: it is frequently present at Berrington, in small

Banded Demoiselle
Calopteryx splendens

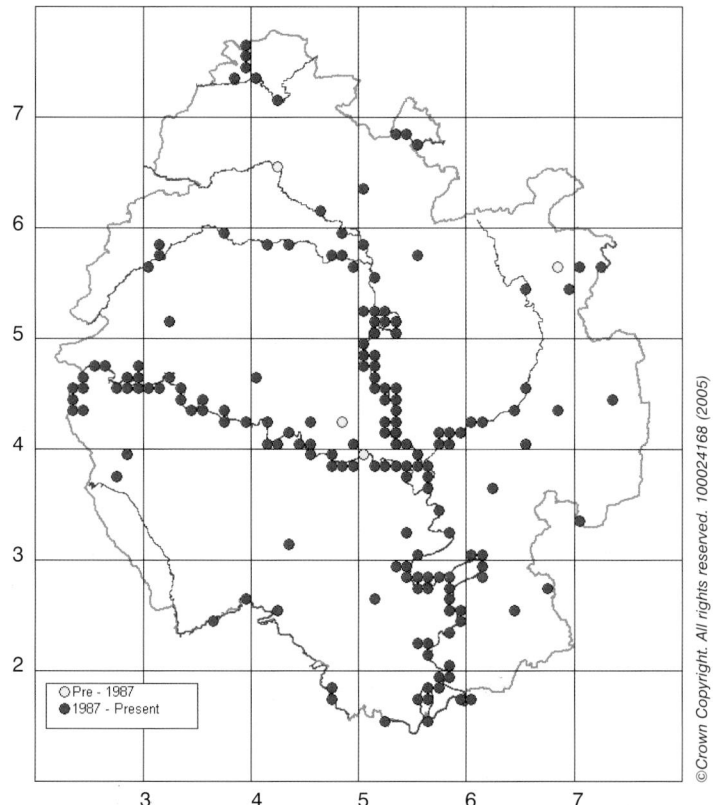

but significant numbers, and it can also be found every year at Bodenham Lake (SO55) and at Trelough Lake on the Whitfield Estate (SO43)

Smaller ponds occasionally get wandering individuals. I have recorded a male Banded Demoiselle in 'splendid' isolation on a pool in the centre of Bringsty Common (SO65), about three miles away from the Teme, which would have been the nearest suitable river. It had set up a territory based on an overhanging leaf of Yellow Flag. From there it made jerky, short circuits along a restricted length of well vegetated poolside bank. I have also recorded lone male Banded Demoiselles totally out of habitat on very small pools close to the Black Mountains (Tyachaf SO23 and Craswell SO23).

Description

The males have a metallic blue/green body which can appear bottle-green at times, depending on the way the sunlight falls upon it. The female abdomen is always green but does show bronze reflections.

The wings of the male have dark-blue wing pigmentation forming a central band, with clear un-pigmented areas towards the bases and tips.

The wings of the females are very lightly tinted green. Three quarters of the way along the costa there is a white, false or psuedo-pterostigma which is twice as large on the fore wing as it is on the hind wing. (false-pterostigma in female Beautiful Demoiselle are the same size on both wings).

It is well known that all Dragonfly species only display their true colours once mature, and then as they approach old age the colour varies according to species, but generally the colours are less bright. I can not think which, if either, of these explanations accounts for a most unusual 'red-form' female Banded Demoiselle that I encountered beside The Wye close to the appropriately named Red Rail Farm near Sellack (SO5528) *(see photo on next page)*. The psuedo-pterostigma allows for confident identification of sex and species.

An immature male Banded Demoiselle can also provide identification difficulties. The adjacent photograph shows an immature male recently emerged and resting a few metres from the river-bank at the confluence of the Lugg and the Wye. I

Male Banded Demoiselle recently emerged and still to develop its distinctive blue patch (or band).

could tell it was male because there were no false pterostigma, but because the pigmentation was not banded I wondered whether I had discovered a site for Beautiful Demoiselle miles from the nearest suitable habitat. In literature there is very little reference to the wing colours of teneral demoiselles, and they are rarely seen because normally they disperse very quickly and hide away in inaccessible vegetation until mature. However, I have little doubt that this is the correct determination for this unusual specimen.

Behaviour

There are few scenes more evocative of the wonders of rural Herefordshire than a wide stretch of the Wye, somewhere between Hereford and Ross, with the shallow water rippling, rushing and swirling between shingle spits and waving plaits of Water-Crowfoot, and the deep blue twinkling 'eyes' on the wings of the Banded Demoiselles dancing close to the surface.

The Banded Demoiselle has a bouncy flight, which can appear quite comical when a procession of males follows a female. The most I have recorded is seven males following one female; this was on the Teme at Little Hereford (SO56) 29th July '97. This can last for several minutes as the female demoiselle leads her suitors a merry dance!

Banded Demoiselle males adopt two strategies to attract a mate. One is to defend a suitable breeding territory in a similar way to most other Dragonfly species. However, unlike most other species he also has a courtship display, which can be seen as one walks along the banks of the Wye. He perches on a prominent leaf and responds to a visiting female by spreading and waving his iridescent wings – flashing his blue patch!!

Beside the Lugg at Shelwick Green (SO54) on 5th July 2003 I found 46 separate wings of Male Banded Demoiselles close together on a muddy 'beach'. All Dragonfly species are prey to a variety of predators and the damselflies and demoiselles are preyed upon by larger dragonflies such as the Emperor, but I suspect that only a bird would have dismembered (or dis-winged) so many insects at the same spot. I noted Kingfisher and Common Sandpiper in the vicinity. The Hobby is well known to dine out on all Dragonfly species, but it catches and eats its prey on the wing so if it had been a Hobby I think the discarded wings would have been distributed over a considerable area. It is possible that the demoiselles were taken at night while they were roosting, but all the wings were from males, which suggests that they were taken while they were flying, because it is the males that fly invitingly over the water as they display and defend their territories. Dan Powell[1] – puts a Spotted Flycatcher into the frame by illustrating a Spotted Flycatcher with a Banded Demoiselle in its beak and the discarded wings falling below it. I was not aware of a Spotted Flycatcher in the vicinity but one might well have been. Wagtails are also possible culprits; I saw both Pied and Grey that morning, but although it would not receive a unanimous guilty vote from the jury, my verdict would be that the Kingfisher was responsible on this occasion.

While contemplating the Banded Demoiselle as a victim I can relate two other observations of note. On 4th August 1996 at Bodenham Lake (SO5250) several Banded Demoiselles were 'mobbing' a Male Emperor Dragonfly, in the way small birds mob a hawk. However, prey turned predator; also at Bodenham I watched a male Banded Demoiselle catch and eat a Common Blue Damselfly.

Unusual all red colouring of a female Banded Demoiselle.

1 Powell D. (1999)

The Emerald Damselfly *Lestes sponsa*

LC

Emerald Damselfly – male.

Flight Period

Most abundant in July and August. This is the last Herefordshire damselfly to emerge, and at some pools in early September it can be the only damselfly still flying. It is remarkable to note that on September 19th 1998 when I recorded the latest date for Emerald Damselfly, the record referred to a pair in the "wheel position"!

Status

National

The Emerald Damselfly has a widespread but patchy distribution throughout Britain and Ireland. In areas where it does not occur it is possible that it has been overlooked but it is more likely to be because of a lack of suitable habitat than for climatic reasons.

Herefordshire – 22/30

Unlike the national picture the distribution of the Emerald Damselfly in Herefordshire shows a clear pattern, with a preponderance of records from the west. The north to south grid line SO50 symmetrically bisects the county. To the east of this line there are just eleven sites for the Emerald Damselfly to the west there are forty-eight. Pools in east Herefordshire

Emerald Damselfly
Lestes sponsa

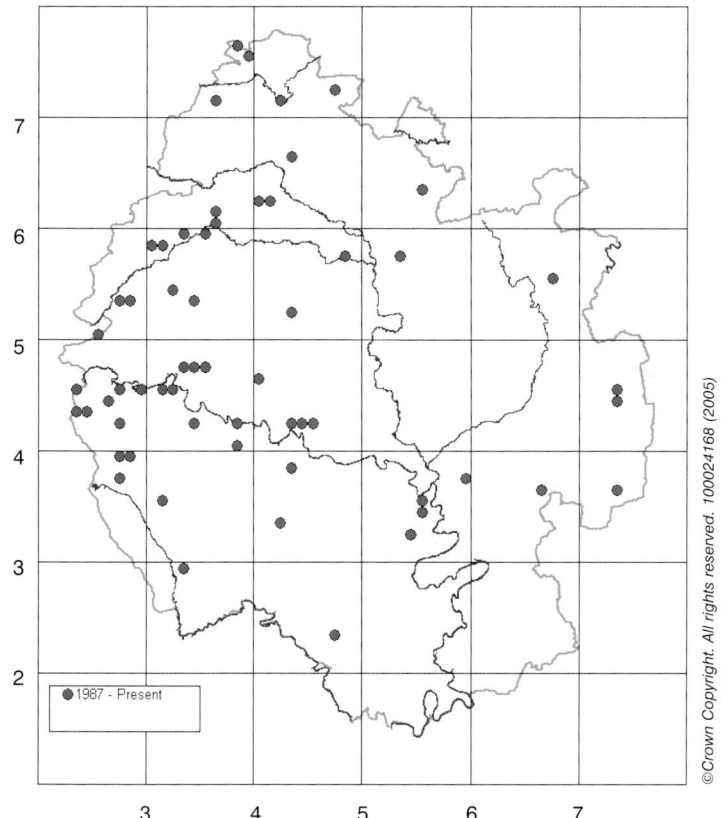

● 1987 - Present

have very similar characteristics to those in the west, but the Emerald Damselfly is found in very few of them. If climate is not a determining factor, I can offer no other explanation. However, when I visit a well vegetated pool in west Herefordshire I expect to find Emerald Damselfly, but when I visit a similar pool in the east I am surprised when I do.

Habitat

Pools of most sizes are favoured so long as they are fringed with tall emergent and marginal vegetation. Shelter in the form of tall hedges or pool side trees is also a feature of most sites. The Emerald Damselfly does not seem to like flying over open water. Most pools frequented by this damselfly have sparse erect vegetation such as Water Horsetail *Equisetum fluviatile* as in the pool on Bromyard Downs (S0670553) or Common Spike-rush *Elecharis palustris* which is the dominant species in a small pool on Cefn Hill (SO278391).

The Azure Damselfly is closely associated with the Emerald Damselfly because they both prefer well vegetated pools, and the Ruddy Darter is also a frequent companion as both Emerald Damselfly and Ruddy Darter can tolerate pools that dry out during very dry spells.

Description

I am normally first alerted to the presence of the Emerald Damselfly by the way it rests with partially open wings. The Irish call it the "Common Spreadwing". The male has bright blue eyes and a metallic green body, with powder-blue segments one and two, and nine and ten, at either end of the abdomen. The same blue is on the lower side of the thorax. To complete these wonderfully matching colours the metallic green of the abdomen becomes increasingly tinged with bronze as the insect matures.

The female lacks the blue pruinescence of the male and can be hard to find when resting well down among the stems of pool-side vegetation. Females also become suffused with bronze towards the end of the season. It is fortunate that with the very late Emerald Damselflies that I had on the 19th of September 1998, the female was joined to the male, which itself was very bronze, because I would not have been able to identify her otherwise: she was a grey/beige colour.

Although their wonderful colours must be observed before one can confidently identify the Emerald Damselfly, it would be unhelpful to include a paragraph on "appearance" without re-emphasising the significance of the "spreadwing" resting pose.

The dark metallic-green female Emerald Damselfly merges well with surrounding Willows.

Behaviour

In comparison to most other damselflies the Emerald tends to sit around more and patrol less. However, they are aggressive and at the pool on Bromyard Downs (mentioned under "Habitat") on the 30th July 2002, I watched attack after attack by male Emerald Damselflies on Blue-tailed Damselflies. As the constantly patrolling Blue-tails flew past a perching Emerald Damselfly it flew out, nipping and butting at the Blue-tail until it was out of territory.

I have only occasionally recorded this damselfly in very large numbers, and even then it never reaches the hundreds or thousands of the common blue damselflies. There were above average densities at Bankfield House Pool on the 4th of August 1996, Chadnor Court on the 10th August 1997 and Summerhill Pools on the 16th August 1997. It is interesting to note they are all dates from the first half of August.

In most concentrations of damselflies, males are far more numerous because the females will be hunting away from the pool, or simply resting – "off duty" before the serious business of mating and ovipositing takes place. However, colonies of Emerald Damselflies are frequently exclusively male or even surprisingly on at least one occasion all female. I presume all the male assemblages (Mathon Gravel Pit – 28th July 2997, Jay Pond 17th July 1999 and Cefn Hill 12th August 2000) were territorial males waiting for the females to arrive, who were probably out of site in surrounding vegetation.

At a small isolated pond in the middle of a wheat field near Little Marcle on the 4th July 1999 there were just a few males beside the water. However, when I walked right round the pond a few metres into the wheat I counted 47 females and just 15 males. However, where could all the males have gone when only females were present at Craswell (7th July 1996) and Stretton Sugwas Gravel Pit (17th June 2000)?

Bankfield House Pool	SO4857
Chadnor Court	SO4352
Summerhill Pools	SO2343
Mathon Gravel Pit	SO7345
Jay Pond	SO3975
Cefn Hill	SO2739
Little Marcle	SO6636
Craswell	SO2737
Stretton Sugwas Gravel Pit	SO4442

The White-legged Damselfly *Platycnemis pennipes*

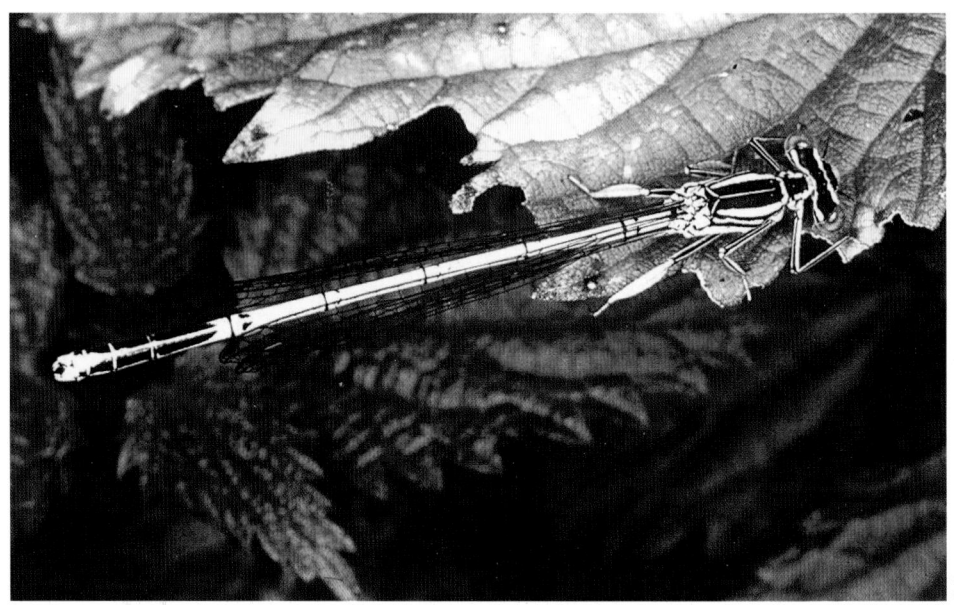

White-legged Damselfly – male

Flight Period

The flight period runs from the second half of May until the end of July. It is most abundant from early June until mid to late July. In 2005 emergence was at least four days later on the Lugg than on the Wye. On the 27th of May there were many beside the Wye at Kings Caple and much further upstream at Winforton. However, there was none beside the Lugg at Hampton Meadow on the 29th and just two on the 30th, not until the 1st of June were they plentiful. Perhaps the Lugg, being a faster flowing river than the Wye, was a little cooler.

Status

National
The White-legged Damselfly is limited in distribution to suitable habitat in southen England, the Midlands as far north as the Wash and east Wales. It is absent from Ireland.

Herefordshire – 18/30
It's linear pattern of distribution in the county traces the courses of Herefordshire's major rivers, with only a few random records marking its inexplicable occurrence at one or two isolated pools.

They are found along the whole length of the Wye in Herefordshire; they can be found further downstream below Monmouth, and further upstream in Radnorshire. In some places in late June and early July they swarm in their thousands in the riverside vegetation and across adjacent fields.

White-legged Damselfly
Platycnemis pennipes

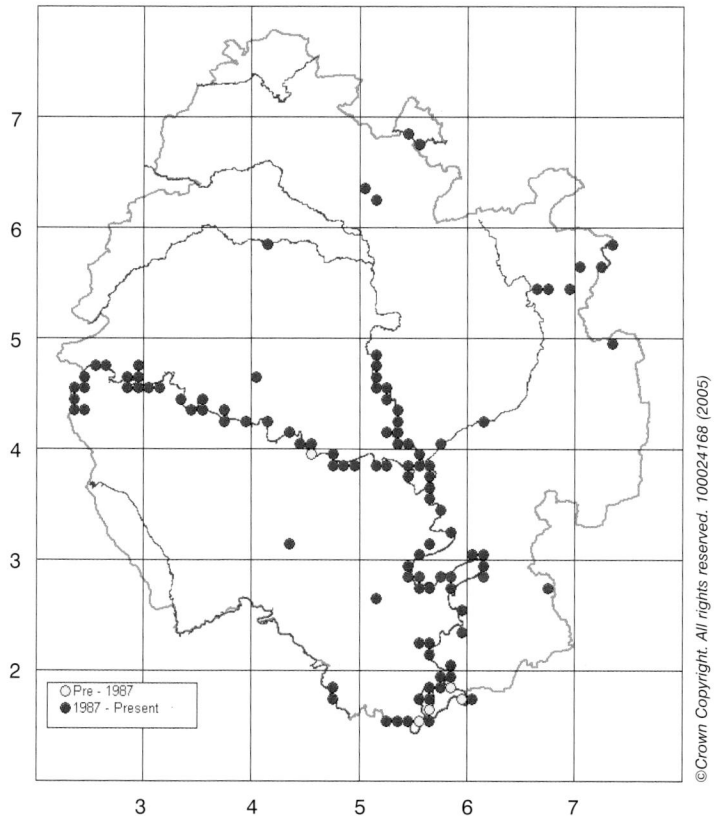

Downstream from the point where the Lugg loops round Dinmore Hill White-legged Damselflies populate the banks of the Lugg as numerously as they do the Wye, but they can not be found upstream from Bodenham.

The Teme flirts with the north-eastern border of Herefordshire and White-legged Damselflies abound beside the Teme downstream from Little Hereford. Similarly the Monnow forms the Southern Herefordshire border and this damselfly can be found at a few suitable spots beside the Monnow.

Habitat

The habitat requirements of the White-legged Damselfly are similar to those of the more widespread and much more conspicuous Banded Demoiselle. They both favour muddy bottomed, gently flowing rivers and streams, but it would seem that White-legged Damselflies are more particular, which presumably explains why their national distribution is much more restricted. This would lead one to believe that they are less tolerant of faster flowing water and they require wider open stretches of river.

They certainly require open sunny stretches of river and they seem to be most plentiful where the river is bordered by wide, open, treeless banks of dense riverside vegetation. They spread into neighbouring fields especially when these comprise of tall meadow grasses and associated herbs or to a lesser extent cereal crops.

Being weaker fliers than Banded Demoiselles the White-legged Damselflies are much less frequently found wandering far from their preferred riverside habitat. However, "riverside habitat "takes on an entirely different meaning in the extreme south of the county. As the Wye prepares to leave Herefordshire it rounds the Great Doward and the limestone pillars of the Seven Sisters tower above it. I have recorded many White-legged Damselflies (both male and female) around these rocks, that rise some 600 feet, almost directly above the river. Many more (mostly females) can be found hunting in the clearings and quarries of The Doward (3rd June 2005 – one or two, 11th June 2005 – several, 18th June 2005 – 100's).

They also occasionally occur on ponds and at two pond sites in Herefordshire they are numerous. I suspect they are breeding at one Trelough Pool on the Whitfield Estate (SO4331) and I have proof of breeding on the other – Queen's Wood Pool in Dymock Forest (SO679273). Where I have observed pre-flight emergents and pairs "incop".

Pond-breeding colonies of White-legged Damselflies are rare so I deemed the Queen's Wood pool worthy of a more detailed habitat description. It is 150m long and 25m wide, bordered on two sides by mixed woodland – mostly conifers, and open to the sunlight on the eastern and southern sides where it abuts a felled area, and a pool side path bounded by shrubs and brambles. There are beds of sedges in places around the margins and around a small island. There are emerging stands of Water Horsetail *Equisetum fluviatile* and patches of Water Lily leaves that provide resting places for a population of Red-eyed Damselflies. On some visits – 5th July 1991, 4th August 1995, 29th June 2003 I have estimated between 50-80 White-legged Damselflies at this woodland pool; most are in the scrubbed over felled area and on the pathside brambles. The Wye, the nearest river is 7km of direct flight from this pool which seems to be the most unlikely habitat for an enduring colony of these river-loving insects!

Description

At a glance, an inexperienced observer might mistake the male White-legged Damselfly for one or other of the commoner "blue" damselflies. However, they appear lighter than any other British damselfly and the dark lines running down the length of the abdomen, as opposed to across it, soon alert one to the difference. The last three segments of the abdomen are dark/black with a thin white central line. This is a conspicuous species indicator in both sexes and throughout the age phases.

As its name suggests, the legs are a creamy white, the tibia is swollen with a thin black central stripe and fringing, well-spaced tapering hairs make the legs resemble tiny feathers.

Males have rather small, but strikingly clear light blue eyes *(see photo at bottom of next page)*.

Females mature from a milky, buff "lactea" phase into very light green replicas of their blue partners. Most colonies contain many of these creamy beige individuals, but the fine black and white streaked abdomen tip ensures there are no identification problems. Tenerals are very pale and almost slightly tinged with pink. They have few of the black markings of the more mature damselflies, except for the distinctive abdominal "tail".

Behaviour

White-legged Damselflies move slowly amongst the shelter of the thick tangle of bankside vegetation which borders open stretches of the Wye. Typically they will fly a little way then rest again, but they will occasionally fly up from cover and disappear high across to the other side of the river.

As is the case with the Banded Demoiselle, with which it shares its riverside quarters, the White-legged Damselfly frequently occurs in high densities which precludes any territorial behaviour. Apart from the Demoiselles it is the only other damselfly to have a courtship display. In a bouncy, fluttering flight it dangles its feathery legs in front of a female. If she is receptive, mating takes place and then the eggs are laid in tandem.

White-legged Damselfly – immature female lactea phase.

Large numbers of paired White-legged Damselflies egg-laying in riverside shallows and lagoons is a common sight along Herefordshire's largest rivers in early June and July. They will cluster around suitable protruding vegetation: the half submerged abdomen of the female curled under the plant stem and the male, firmly gripping her behind the head with his anal claspers, standing erect above her. Ten to twenty pairs ovipositing in this way are a detailed quintessence of the Wye.

So great are their numbers along some stretches of river that they fly up in clouds (perhaps more literally, "in their tens") at one's feet as one walks through long grass beside the river, or through a neighbouring meadow.

The White-legged Damselfly is often quoted in the literature as being susceptible to pollution. If this is the case, there can be no concern for the environmental health of the rivers Wye and Lugg!

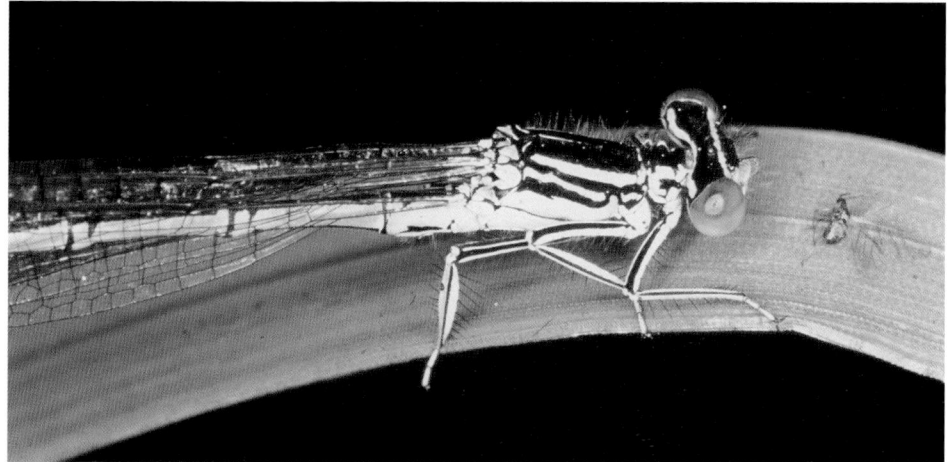

The bright blue eyes size up an aphid.

The Large Red Damselfly *Pyrrhosoma nymphula*

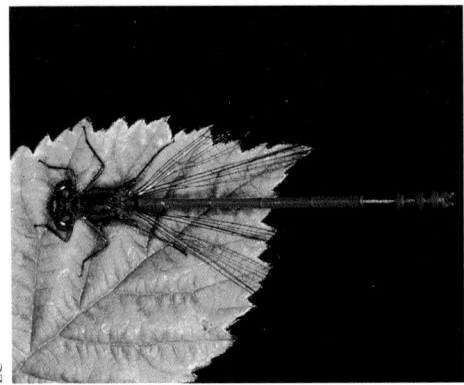

LC   LC

Large Red Damselfly – male.   *Large Red Damselfly – female.*

Flight Period

Most abundant in May and June with numbers dropping off very quickly in July, but a few individuals sometimes surviving into August.

This is almost always the first damselfly or dragonfly to be seen in the spring. 2003 was an early year and the 14th April was exceptional. Most years the first Large Reds are seen during the last few days of April or the first few of May. In 2000 the last Large Red Damselfly that I saw was on 18th June even though I searched many sites where they usually occur. I assumed their early demise was the result of cold, wet springs that year.

Status

National
Common and widespread across all of Britain and Ireland, although not found in such profusion as is sometimes the case with one or two of the common blue damselflies.

Herefordshire – 30/30
Widespread across the county on almost all unpolluted sunny water but in low densities – as frequently found on rivers streams and brooks as on ponds and lakes.

Habitat

All sunny unpolluted pools and most streams and rivers, but it can be absent at new pools without emergent or marginal vegetation. It certainly favours well vegetated sites.

Description

There is virtually no chance of misidentification of the Large Red Damselfly in Herefordshire because it is the only red damselfly which occurs in the county. However, its

Large Red Damselfly
Pyrrhosoma nymphula

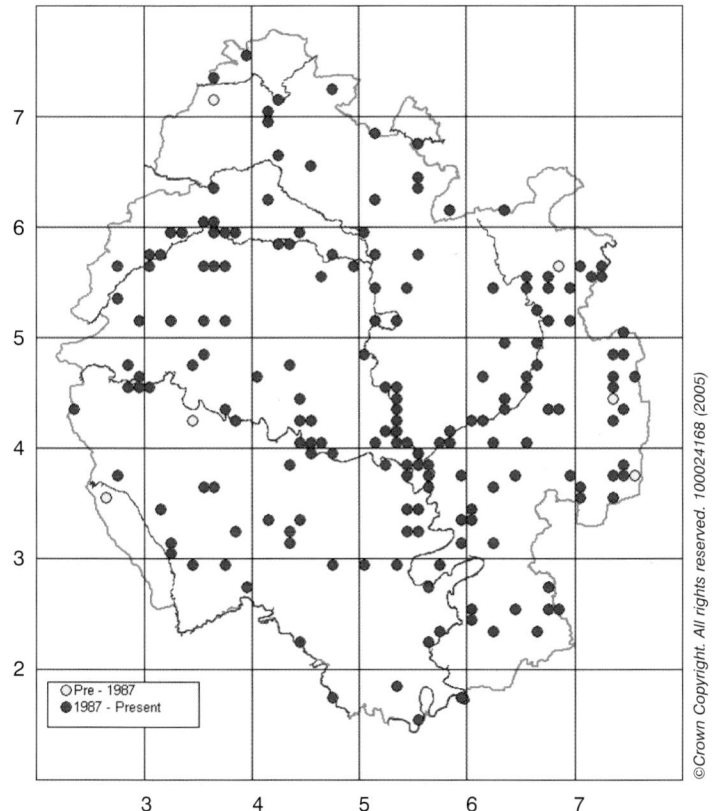

Legend:
- ○ Pre - 1987
- ● 1987 - Present

name is slightly misleading because it is only 'large' in relation to the Small Red Damselfly which is a scarce acid bog specialist. Not only has the Small Red not been recorded in Herefordshire, but neither has it been seen in any of our neighbouring counties.

I have received several records from people with garden ponds and I have felt confident about entering them onto the database even when the observer claims no specialist knowledge, because a bright red damselfly in spring or early summer must be the Large Red.

The male is a red and black damselfly with some bronze tints especially near the end of the abdomen. The female is slightly more robust than the male, has more black on her abdomen and the yellow/bronze tints are more widespread. There are three recognised forms of the female: F. *melanotum* has an almost black abdomen, except for very small areas of red and bronze,and it has yellow rather than red thorasic stripes; I have recorded this form on two or three occasions at Mathon Gravel Pits, but it appears to be rare in the count:. F. *intermedia* and F. *fulvipes* also vary in the amount of black on the abdomen, with the latter having the least black. Unfortunately I have not distinguished between these two forms in my recording and consequently can not comment on their distribution in Herefordshire, but both forms were together at Queen's Wood Pool – Dymock (SO679273) on the 7th May 2005 – *see photos below*.

Behaviour

I have never found Large Red Damselflies in the large concentrations that one frequently finds The Common Blue, White-legged or Azure Damselflies, and they are more often found in marginal and bordering vegetation rather than flying over the water surface. They oviposit in tandem and they are often found flying or settled on vegetation as a joined pair. I have recorded the Emperor hunting Large Reds to the exclusion of all others, even when they have been relatively scarce and others, the Azure Damselfly in particular, have been abundant (for more details read 'behaviour notes' for The Emperor).

At Stretton Sugwas Gravel Pit I caught a Large Red Damselfly making improper advances towards an immature orange phase Scarce Blue-tailed Damselfly (for more details read behaviour notes for that species).

F. *fulvipes*   F. *intermedia*

The Red-eyed Damselfly *Erythromma najas*

Red-eyed Damselfly – male

Flight Period
First emerging at the very end of May, the Red-eyed Damselfly remains on the wing until mid-August, but it is most abundant in June and July.

Status

National
It is most common in southeastern England, but it is widespread throughout the rest of southern England and the Midlands except for the southwest peninsular. It extends north as far as Cheshire in the west and southeast Yorkshire in the east. It is not found in Scotland or Ireland and the only Welsh population is a well-established colony on the Montgomery Canal.

Herefordshire – 10/30
I have tried to be quite specific about the national distribution of the Red-eyed Damselfly because it would appear that Herefordshire is a "frontier" county. With just thirteen colonies scattered across the north and east of the county, and many suitable looking ponds, especially in the south and west, where it is absent, it is reasonable to describe our colonies as being at the extreme western edge of this damselfly's range.

Habitat
Red-eyed Damselflies in Herefordshire only occur on large ponds and lakes. Elsewhere in the country they are recorded from canals and very slow-flowing rivers. All the Herefordshire sites have water-lillies (White-*Nymphaea*, Yellow-*Nuphar lutea* and Fringed-*Nymphoides peltata*) or Broad-leaved Pondweed *(Potamogeton natans)* providing large

Red-eyed Damselfly
Erythromma najas

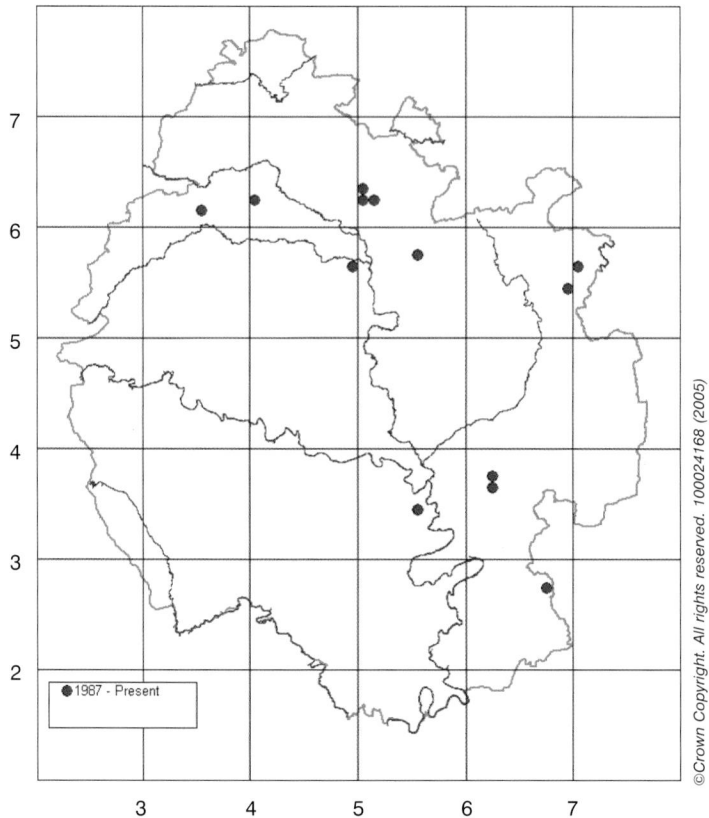

floating leaves for the males to lie-out on. The pools need to be quite large because the males like to sit well out from the shore, but they do all seem to be sheltered; often close to woodland.

Description

This is, by far, my favourite damselfly. I get a leap of excitement when I scan with my binoculars across a pool with floating water-lily leaves and pick up two small, bright, wine-red, beed-like eyes. Not only is it a scarce damselfly in the county, but I consider it to be the most attractive as well.

It is slightly larger than any of the others and the limited pruinose, slightly powdery blue markings contrast with the very dark, almost black abdomen and the bronze-black dorsal surface of the thorax and the last two segments of the abdomen. This blue tip can lead to confusion with the slightly smaller Blue-tailed Damselfly, but with that species the blue is like a band or a patch on the second segment from the end; with the Red-eyed Damselfly the blue forms a clear tip as if it has been dipped in paint.

Females are much less easy to spot. Not only are her eyes a dull red (barely noticable), but she lacks the blue sides to the thorax and worst of all; she has no blue tail. Whereas the dark colouration of the male is a very dark-blue, the female is very dark-green. I have read that this can lead to confusion with female Emerald Damselfly but I have never seen them that way.

Immatures of both sexes are a light yellowy green-straw colour. I have only picked out females or immatures after I have first seen a male.

Behaviour

Lying out on water-lily leaves is by far the most distinctive behaviour associated with the male Red-eyed Damselfly. They are aggressive towards other males. You will very rarely see two sat on the same leaf! They will also chase off other species of damselfly, although I have seen Red-eyed Damselfly and Blue-tailed Damselfly perched close together on Fringed Water-lily and it was helpful to note the difference in size and "tail" pattern.

When they leave their leaf they fly low and direct across the water surface. Even when they fly beside the shore they will always fly back towards the middle of the pond before they settle again. This is immensely frustrating for a photographer. However while walking around Berrington Pool (SO5162) on the 19th June 2004, looking for the elusive Variable Damselfly I came across many Red-eyed Damselflies in the pool-side vegetation. The sun was in and out from behind the clouds and when I found them it had been clouded for some time. Presumably, in adverse weather conditions they seek the shelter of marginal, or probably even more distant vegetation.

Even in sunny weather you are more likely to find the dark and featureless females concealed in fringing vegetation.

They oviposit in tandem, often descending below water to insert eggs in water-lily stems. I observed a pair in tandem on the Lawn Pool, Brockhampton (SO5954) on the 5th of August 2000 and they remained underwater for just over 15 minutes. Remarkable as this seems to me I understand that it wouldn't even reach half way in the record books for submerged Red-eyed Damselflies!

By way of a summary

When you come across a good sized pool with plenty of large-leaved floating vegetation, look for a dark, larger than normal damselfly, either sat on a lily leaf or flying low over the water, acting aggressively towards other damselflies, with a bright blue tail. If you think you have identified a likely candidate focus your binoculars on it and check for the piercing red eyes! I'm sure there are more Herefordshire sites for this damselfly still to be discovered.

Red-eyed Damselfly – female

The Azure Damselfly *Coenagrion puella*

Azure Damselfly – male

Flight Period

The Azure Damselfly is seen in great numbers from the last week in May until the end of July. As with the Common Blue Damselfly, populations build towards the end of May, but the Azure's flight period does not last as long as that of the Common Blue Damselfly. They become scarce in August and I have only once recorded one in September.

Status

National
Common and widespread in lowland Britain, but absent from northern Scotland. It is not uncommon in much of Ireland, but has a patchy distribution there.

Herefordshire – 30/30
Very common at most sites, but more particular about its choice of pools than the Common Blue Damselfly.

Azure Damselfly
Coenagrion puella

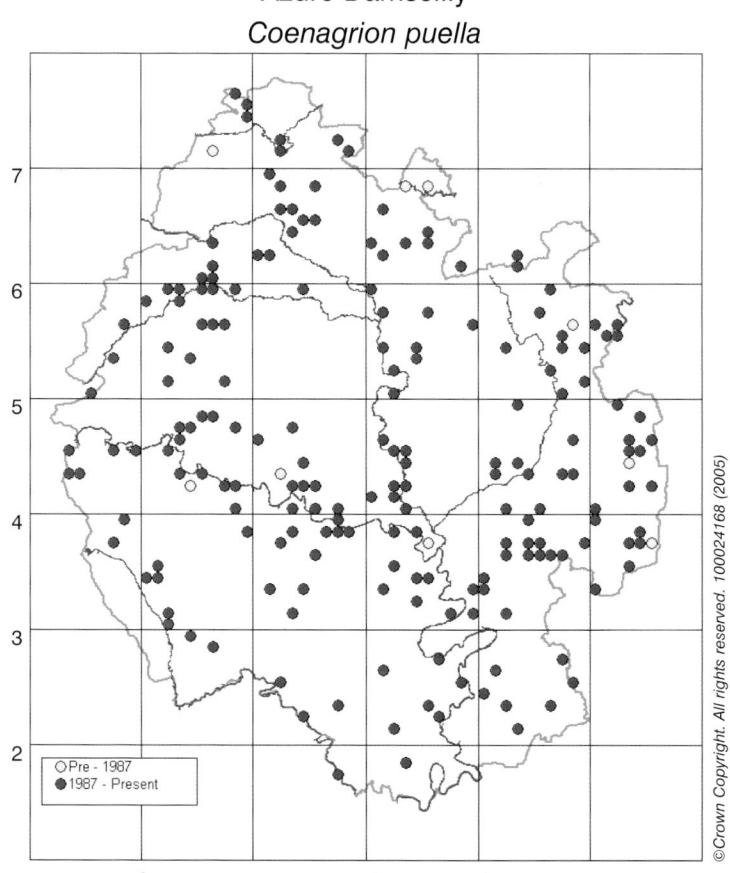

Legend: ○ Pre - 1987 ● 1987 - Present

Habitat

The Azure Damselfly is found in a wide range of habitats in Herefordshire, but it is most numerous in the smaller, sheltered, well vegetated pools – including many garden ponds. It is less likely to be seen at large open water bodies, especially recently created pools with little or no marginal vegetation.

It is often found in riverside vegetation (although it is unlikely to be breeding in running water unless it is very slow flowing) and can also be seen some distance away from water in wet meadows and rough grassland. It is interesting to speculate on the origins of a male Azure Damselfly found in vegetation beside the Lugg just up-stream from Mordiford (SO53) as early as the 15th May 2005. The river flows swiftly at this point and there don't appear to be any ponds nearby!

Description

In Herefordshire this blue damselfly is only likely to be confused with the Common Blue Damselfly. The Azure Damselfly is a member of the genus – *Coenagrion*, which comprises several very similar blue damselflies that can be particularly difficult to separate. However, apart from the Azure, the others are all either rare or local: only one – the Variable Damselfly – has been recorded in Herefordshire and that is only at one site. *(To separate Azure and Variable Damselflies see notes under Variable Damselfly).*

The Azure is a blue or black damselfly with thin antehumeral stripes (broad in the Common Blue) and a rather angular U shaped mark on the second segment of the abdomen (a stalked dot on the Common Blue *(see photo on page 65)*. This mark can be seen quite easily as the damselflies settle in the pool side vegetation.

The females are normally black and green (much more black than green) but about 10% of all females are homochrone (coloured like males) *see photo below*. As with many species of damselfly it is safer to identify the females by catching them and checking detailed diagnostic features in the hand, but this is not normally necessary because of the presence of many males. The green females appear black from above with thin green rings between all the abdominal segments, except the last two which are blue. The sides of the thorax are green with two very narrow black diagonal lines, and the side view of the abdomen is green.

In both sexes the antehumeral stripes are narrow.

Behaviour

Azure Damselflies can be found in swarming numbers around the margins of pools, many resting on rushes and other tall pool-side vegetation. Frequently, they are joined in tandem or mating in the 'wheel position'. Being weak flyers and enjoying the shelter of marginal vegetation it is not surprisingly, they are the most frequently ensnared species in cobwebs.

They do not usually fly for long, but make short flights before settling again. This provides plenty of opportunities to look closely at them, note the U shape on segment 2 and the narrow antehumeral stripes, and in this way confirm identification.

LC

Azure Damselfly – female (blue form).

The Variable Damselfly *Coenagrion pulchellum*

Flight Period

The flight period extends from the end of May to the beginning of August, but they are most likely to be seen in June and July. The only Herefordshire record was on 31st July 1996

Status

National
Scarce, with a scattered distribution of restricted localised colonies randomly occurring across England, Wales and south-western Scotland. Paradoxically, it is common and widespread in Ireland.

Herefordshire – 1/30
I have searched throughout the county at many seemingly suitable sites for this insect, but have never found it. Last year I received information that in 1996 a very distinguished entomologist discovered a small number (3 or 4) of Variable Damselflies at the southern end of the lake at Berrington Hall (National Trust property) (SO5063). Matthew Oates was working for the National Trust at the time and explained that he was well acquainted with this damselfly from time spent earlier in his life in Hampshire and Sussex.

I visited Berrington Pool on three separate occasions during June and July 2004 (the first season after I heard about Matthew Oates' record) but I found no sign of the Variable Damselfly. It is a large lake with a long margin; if it is a weak colony with a small population I might well have missed it. On the other hand, it is very difficult to distinguish from the Azure Damselfly and I have had no previous experience of spotting it, so I might have overlooked it. I shall search again in 2005. It would be presumptive to dismiss it as extinct in Herefordshire. Furthermore, I still retain ambitions of discovering it elsewhere in the county.

Habitat

From the literature, it is difficult to see how the habitat requirements for the Variable Damselfly differ from those of the Azure. Perhaps they prefer slightly more overgrown pools than the Azure. They certainly like unpolluted, well vegetated, sheltered, still water. In other parts of the country there can be large numbers at one site, then none at all at another seemingly identical site within close proximity. It would seem there is still much to discover about this enigmatic damselfly.

Description

The Variable Damselfly is very similar to the Azure, and great care must be taken with identification. Those who are familiar with it, explain that it looks darker than the Azure because the blue markings are more restricted. The mark on segment two of the abdomen is described as a wine glass, rather than a U symbol; the U being joined to the base with a stem *(see opposite page)*. Unfortunately, the Azure Damselfly can have a stalked U. Although this is extremely rare I did find a damselfly on the disused canal at Monkhide (SO64) on 23rd July 1995 which had a 'wine glass' mark on section two of the abdomen. I was naturally, very excited and believed I had found the Variable Damselfly. However, I caught this insect and checked out all the other features to be sure.

Variable Damselfly
Coenagrion pulchellum

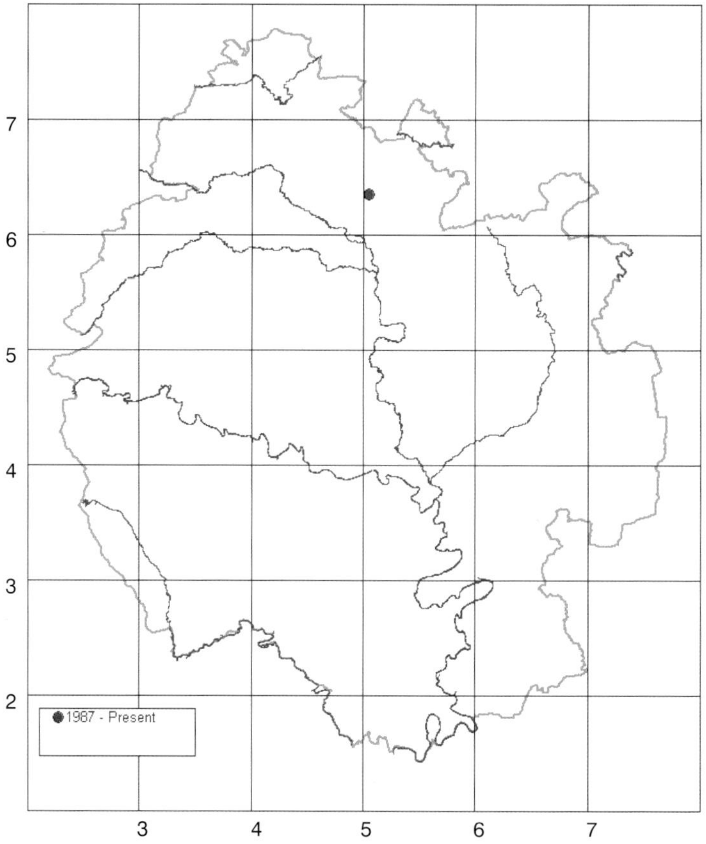

● 1987 - Present

1) The 'wine glass' shape on abdomen segment 2 ✓
2) The antehumeral stripes were discontinuous
   and looked like exclamation marks [!!] This is the most
   distsinctive feature and the one most likely to be seen
   as it moves about in poolside vegetation. ✗
3) The hind margin of the pronotum is strongly three lobed ✗
4) Segment 9 of the abdomen is almost entirely black ✗

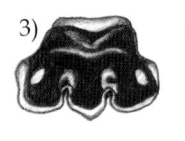

Variable Damselfly

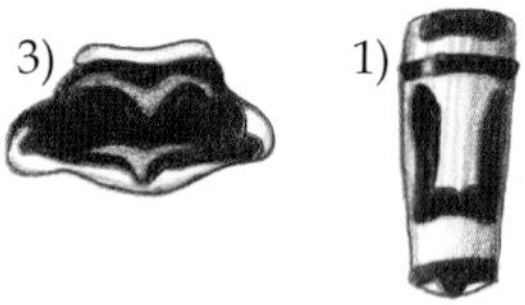

To be certain of one's identification of this damselfly one must study these detailed but vital features. The strongly three lobed hind margin of the pronotum is the most reliable diagnostic feature. With my 'Monkhide' damselfly only the 'wineglass' feature pointed to Variable Damselfly, the other important features all indicated Azure Damselfly, which is what it undoubtedly must have been.

Azure Damselfly

The Common Blue Damselfly *Enallagma cyathigerum*

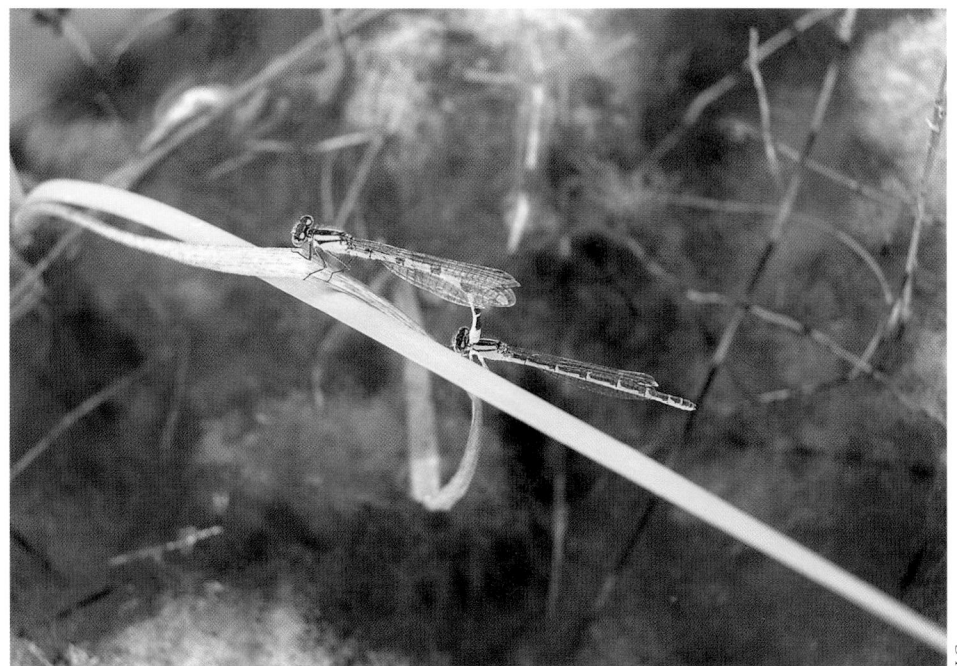

Male and female (blue form in tandem)

Flight Period
Flying from May to September but seen in greatest numbers from mid-May to mid-August

Status

National
Widely distributed and common across all of Britain and Ireland, and indeed considered to be one of the commonest species of damselfly or dragonfly in the world.[1]

Herefordshire – 29/30
Widespread and common

Habitat
It is found on most unpolluted and sunny pools, canals, ditches and even slow flowing rivers and streams in Herefordshire.

---

1 Merritt R., et al. 1996

Common Blue Damselfly
Enallagma cyathigerum

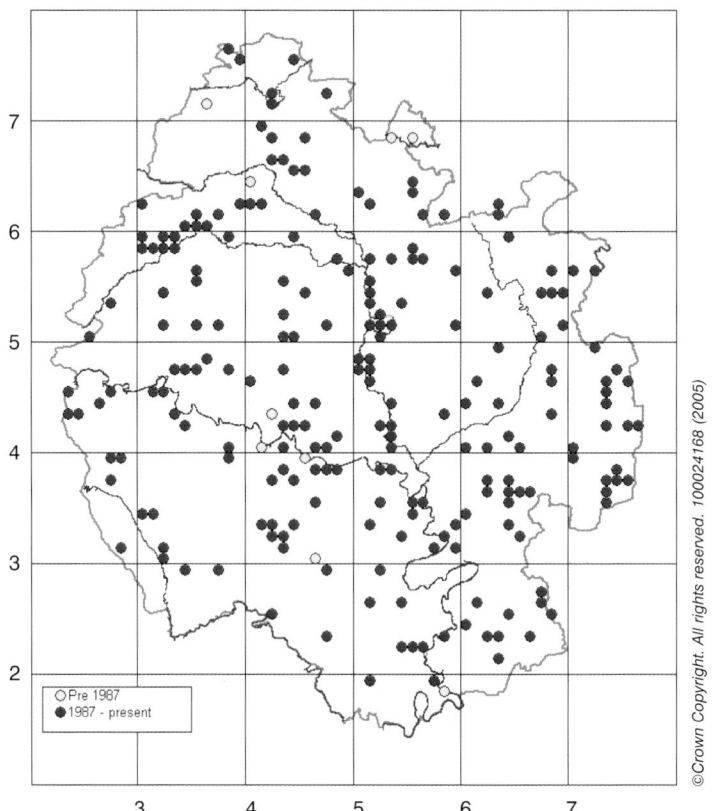

In peak season there can be swarms of Common Blue Damselflies at favoured spots. These tend to be the larger, more open pools and lakes, whereas the Azure, which is very similar in appearance and almost as ubiquitous, prefers smaller, well vegetated sites, because it is a weaker flyer.

The Common Blue is sometimes the only damselfly present at some of the larger, more open waters such as the newly formed lakes at Mathon, Wellington and Stretton Sugwas Gravel Pits, but it does still require submerged beds of aquatic vegetation to give shelter for the larvae. Thread-leaved pondweeds – *Potamogeton bercholdii* and *P. pusilum* along with some of the Starworts – *Callitriche* sp are often the first colonists of such habitats.

Although I very often find them beside rivers I think it is unlikely that they breed in many of the Herefordshire rivers or streams.

Description

Of all the blue damselflies the Common Blue is the bluest. However, one must be careful when identifying the superficially similar blue damselflies; confusion with the genus

Coenagrion (which in Herefordshire almost exclusively means the Azure Damselfly) is most likely; attention to detail is essential. It has broad blue antehumeral stripes and a distinctive stalked round, or oval, spot on the second segment of the abdomen *(see photo below)*. The broad stripes (as opposed to narrow in the Azure) on top of the thorax can be seen from further away (even sometimes in flight), but it takes experience to recognise the difference in thickness of these stripes. The shape of the mark on the second abdominal segment is more difficult to see but is diagnostic. On more than one occasion I have found a Common Blue with an unstalked oval spot. This still allows no confusion with the Azure, and it is quite widely described in literature as an unusual form.

On the female the black of the abdomen is far more extensive than on the male. There are blue and green forms of females: the colour shows more clearly from the side rather than from above when they look mainly dark. Further confusion can arise because the young (teneral) females are a light straw colour and then the green or blue forms gradually turn to brown with age. The antehumeral stripes, whether green or blue, are thick on both sexes, so this can be helpful with females, but whenever possible it is advisable to confirm the presence of this species by identifying the male – there are normally plenty of them about! If one catches the female in a net there is an obvious spine in front of the ovipositor which is unique to the female Common Blue Damselfly.

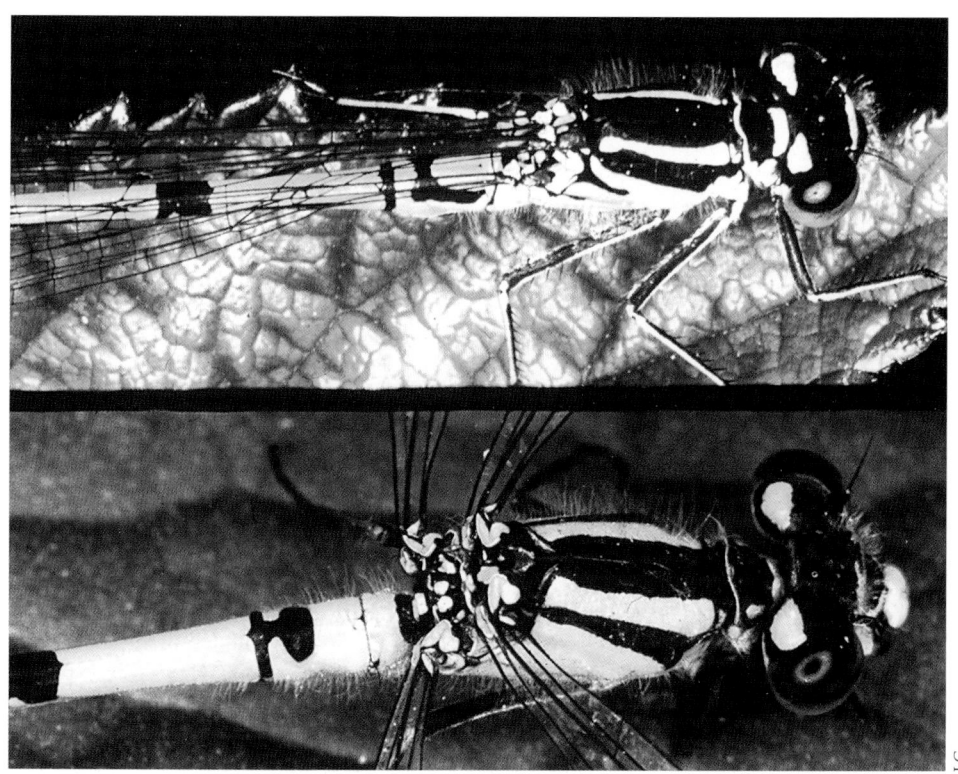

Azure Damselfly above and Common Blue Damselfly below, showing the different mark on abdominal segment two and the narrower antehumeral stripes on the Azure.

Behaviour

As damselflies go, the Common Blue is a 'toughie'. They fly out over open water, sometimes well away from the shore and frequently in tandem. They can also be seen hunting over meadows, rough grassland and along hedges and woodland edges.

Males fly purposefully, close to the water's surface when defending their territory, and can be aggressive with other males when vying for a mate. A typical site, well populated with Common Blue Damselflies will include, some moving in and out of marginal vegetation, others resting flat on bare ground close to the water's edge, many patrolling low across the surface of the lake or pool, some flying in tandem, others in the wheel-position and some standing vertical to the water with the female joined below, ovipositing. Yet more will be resting horizontally perched on emergent stems of aquatic plants such as Water Millfoil *Myriophyllum sp.* or Water Horsetail *Equisetum fluviatile* or Spike Rush *Eleocharis sp.*

When the weather is bad, or at night, these damselflies will roost together on the stems of emergent and marginal vegetation and frequently they are all aligned facing into the wind.

Where Common Blue and Azure Damselflies are both at the same pool, as is often the case, there will be more Common Blues flying out over the pool and more Azures will be amongst the pool-side vegetation.

Both were present in considerable numbers at Whiterralls Pool near Weobley (SO35) on 1st June 1999. There was a bare, beaten track along the western side of the pool with a row of trees, tall grasses, nettles and brambles between the path and the pool. Many Common Blues were basking flat on the hard smooth track surface, while just as many Azures were hanging vertically from bordering vegetation.

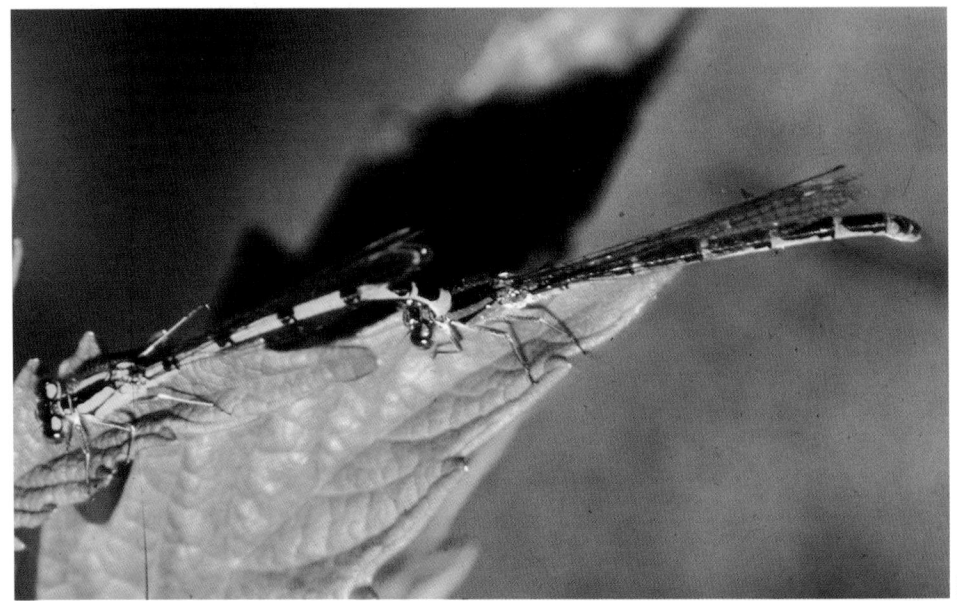

LC

Male and female (green form in tandem).

Scarce Blue-tailed Damselfly *Ischnura pumilio*

LC

Scarce Blue-tail – male

Flight Period

From my experience of the only Herefordshire site, the last few days in May and the first couple of weeks in June is the only time they can be seen in good numbers. Presumably many are lost early due to their instictive urge to disperse – *see notes under 'Behaviour'*. Nationally they are on the wing from late May until early September, with a July peak expected.

Status

National
This is a scarce damselfly with most sites in the south and west of England and Wales, There are no modern records from the east or north of England and it is not known from Scotland. It has a widespread, scattered distribution in Ireland.

Herefordshire – 1/30
Stretton Sugwas Gravel Pit in central Herefordshire (SO4442) is the only known site in the county for this inconspicuous insect. Since the Scarce Blue-tailed Damselfly was discovered in 1999 it has been recorded there annually. Most years there have been 20 – 30 damselflies present (on 31-05-00 many were emerging and I estimated that there was a minimum of 50) but in 2004 only one or two were found. This could have just been a 'bad' year; they might have emerged earlier or later than usual and I missed the peak, or it could be signalling the end of the colony because the water table in this former gravel pit is dropping.

In 2005 the flush had less water than ever (even in a hot August) but there were a few emerging Scarce Blue-tails – 3 or 4 pale *'aurantiaca phase* females' and one very bright one. On a neighbouring, shallow, flooded "Spike-rush area" there were two or three mature males.

Scarce Blue-tailed Damselfly
Ischnura pumilio

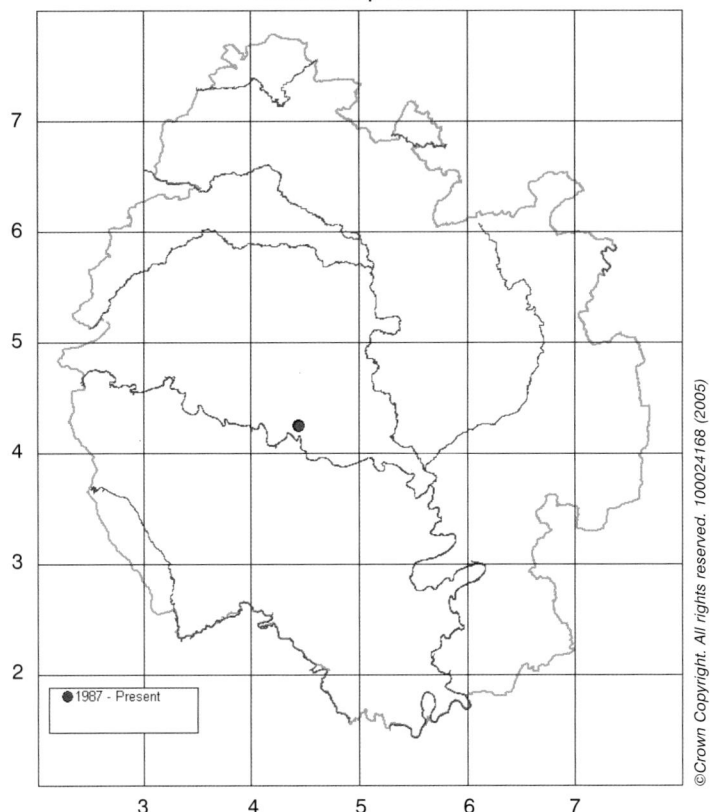

Habitat

The Scarce Blue-tail has very specialised habitat requirements. Colonies are often small and isolated: it is difficult to imagine where the nearest colony to our Herefordshire gravel pit might be! They need shallow, very slow-moving or occasionally still water with a soft muddy or silty bottom and sparse vegetation.

It would appear that extraction industries have provided suitable habitats for the Scarce Blue-tail and as a result it has been found in chalk pits and gravel pits in parts of southern England away from its south-westerly strongholds. The Herefordshire site in a disused gravel pit is very typical of this species. As this is considered to be a nationally scarce species and there is much still to be discovered about it, I considered it worthwhile to describe the Herefordshire site in detail.

A network of shallow pools remain at the gravel pit. One, which is about the size of two tennis courts, and barely more than a metre at its deepest is fed in the north-west corner from a spring which has been disturbed by earlier gravel extraction. This gravel extraction ceased at this end of the gravel pit in the late 1980s. The pool is very exposed , with no trees or shrubs nearby, and as it is in an area which is regularly grazed by cattle there is no tall emergent vegetation. However, it is afforded some shelter because it is surrounded by gently sloping banks which are the result of landscaping.

I discovered the Scarce Blue-tails on the first of June 1999 in the marshy north-west corner where the spring fed seepage feeds the pool. Here there was much more vegetation. The water runs quite quickly from the source for about a metre before fanning out to form a delta some ten metres long and four wide at the point where it enters the pool. After the initial metre the flow is almost imperceptible.

In this swampy delta there is a mixture of low aquatic plants and a few which grow to about two feet. The tallest was Hard Rush, *Juneus inflexus*, which sparsely populated the seepage area and there was one clump of Soft Rush *J. effusus*. There were quite a few plants of Great Willowherb *Epilobium hirsutum* already half a metre tall and destined to grow taller unless they are grazed. Another taller plant was Blue Water-speedwell *Veronica anagallis-aquatica* which was in flower and quite plentiful, and there were a few plants of Water Plantain *Alisma plantago-aquatica* but nothing else that would grow above a metre.

Common Spike-rush *Eleocharis palustris* and Jointed Rush *Juncus articulatus* dominated much of the ground cover with the large leaves of Coltsfoot *Tussilago farfara* confined to the drier margins. Some patches contained Small Sweet-grass *Glyceria declinata* with some Rough Meadow-grass *Poa trivialis* mixed in with it. Tufted Forget-me-not *Myosotis laxa* was well established throughout the area and there were odd flowers of Creeping Buttercup *Ranunculus repens* dotted here and there. Celery-leaved Buttercup *R. sceleratus* was quite common, especially close to where the delta joined the main pool. In the places where the water was deepest, up to about 35 cm, there was a thick choking growth of Stonewort *Chara sp*. All of this delta area has recently been trodden and lightly grazed by cattle. The smell of their dung on the drying banks was pungent. The grazing of the cattle prevents the vegetation from growing too tall and thick. This would shade the water which needs to warm quickly from direct sunlight. Furthermore the hooves of the cattle help to keep the substrata soft.

Azure Damselfly, Blue-tailed Damselfly and, to a lesser extent, Large Red Damselfly and the Scarce Blue-tailed Damselfly were all well represented in the seepage, but the Scarce Blue-tail was probably the dominant species. I estimated that there were about thirty individuals present.

I searched all the other possible areas within the confines of the gravel pit but found no more Scarce Blue-tails. One spring-fed seepage was steeper with a significantly faster flow and had a harder substrata which meant there was little more than a surface film of water, much of which was covered with a thick carpet of Marsh Horsetail *Equisetum palustre*. Another seepage was very soft and squelchy but was choked with above-waist high vegetation and was in the early stages of colonisation by willows *Salix sp*. This seepage was fenced off – if the cattle could get to it to graze it, it would probably be suitable for Scarce Blue-tails *(see photo bottom right of opposite page)*.

There were extensive flat areas with about 10 cm of water where Common Spike-rush was growing profusely but none of these areas had Scarce Blue-tails. They were not spring-fed so there was no flow and they would probably dry up in the summer and probably freeze in winter. It should be noted that there was plenty of water throughout the area at this time because of recent very heavy rain.

Later in the year (1st August 1999), I returned to this site at the end of a very hot dry spell. The pool had shrunk to a half of its early summer size but the spring was still feeding the seepage. The 'delta' was marshy but was clearly replenishing the pool at a slower rate than the loss of water through evaporation. There was a herd of eighty cows seeking the

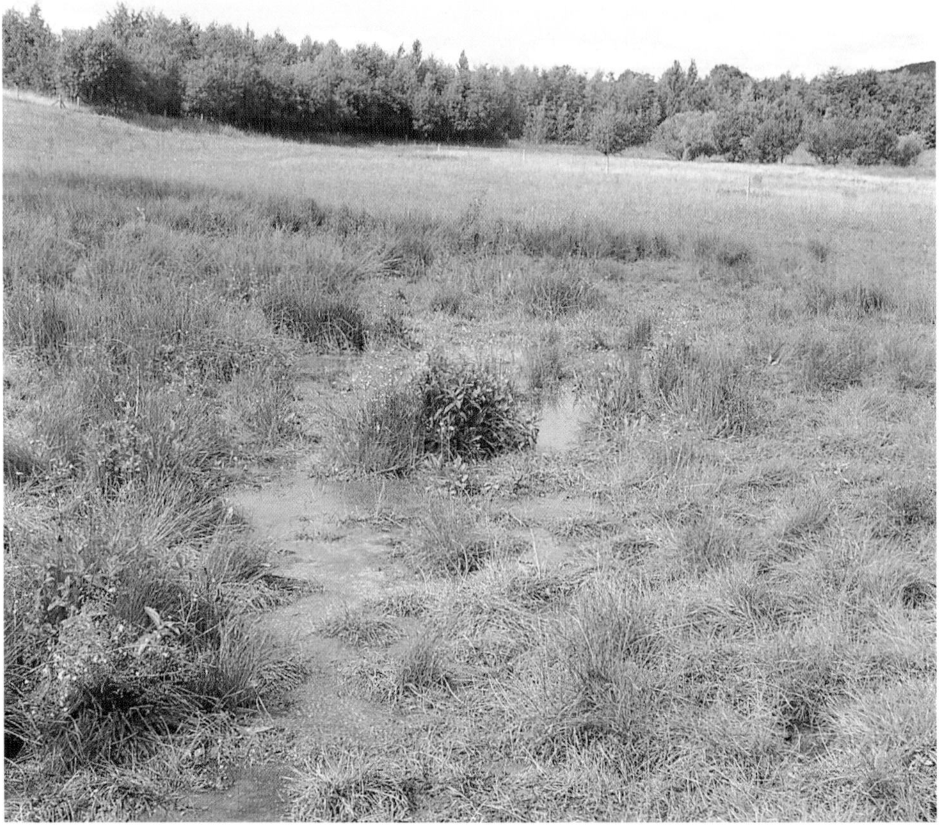

PGG

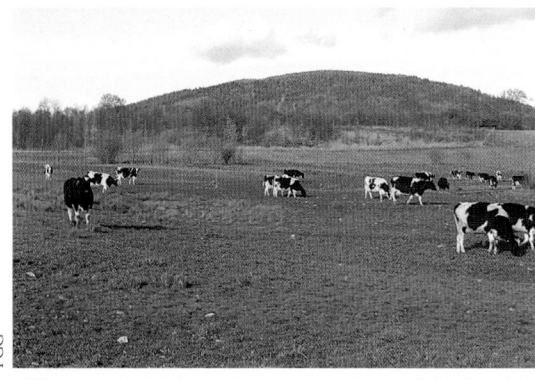

The "Scarce Blue-tail flush" at Stretton Sugwas in mid August.

PGG

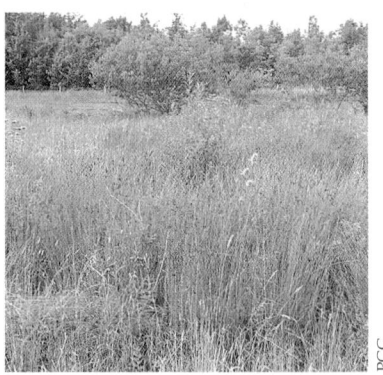

The same flush in November –grazing is essential to keep it open and free from choking vegetation.

PGG

A nearby flush which is not grazed is unsuitable for the Scarce Blue-tail.

solace of the pool in the heat of the day and it seemed remarkable to me that the larva of the Scarce Blue-tail could survive amongst the heavily trodden and heavily manured marsh of the seepage. Everywhere had been much more heavily grazed than at my previous visit. Despite the uninviting nature of this spot, I noted the Four-spotted Chaser hovering over the 'delta' and two coupled pairs of Emerald Damselflies, seeking a place to egg-lay.

This unique habitat, although unprepossessing to the eyes of a human, is clearly of considerable attraction to more than one species of Dragonfly! In subsequent years the water-table has dropped throughout the area of the gravel pit but the seepage has never completely dried up, and cycles of grazing have continued to keep the flush open.

Description

Scarce Blue-tailed Damselflies are very similar in appearance to Blue-tailed Damselflies. They are smaller and have a weaker flight, but they can easily be confused and so any suspected Scarce Blue-tail should be netted and closely examined. As can be seen in the photograph below, abdominal segment nine on the Scarce Blue-tail is all blue, with two very small black markings and only the hind margin of segment eight is blue, whereas in the Blue-tailed Damselfly just segment eight is blue and it is entirely blue.

The extent and nature of the black markings on the blue background of segment nine can vary. Most field guides describe two small black dots, or sometimes commas[1]. Some of the Scarce Blue-tails in Herefordshire have small dots or commas, but almost half have square brackets as shown in the photograph on the previous page. The only reference that I can find to this is a series of illustrations drawn from slides of live individuals photographed in the New Forest by Wickstead[2]. These show 8 variations, and the Stretton Sugwas "square bracket specimen" is like the one they have marked 'D'. Unfortunately, there is no text, which might inform as to the prevalence of each form. Apart from the dots and commas I

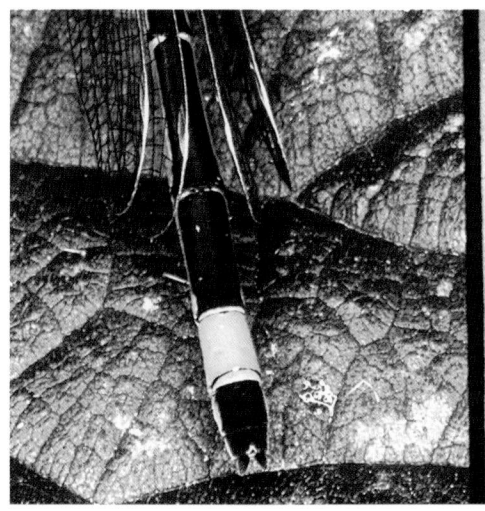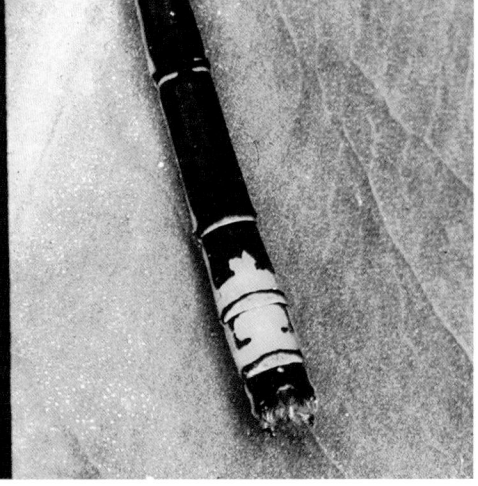

Blue-tail   Scarce Blue-tail
Showing the diagnostically different tail patterns

---

1   Shown with square brackets in Powell D. 1999 and Gibbons B. 1986
2   Wickstead A.R. and N.I. 1983

have found none of the other 'Wickstead variations'. All the Welsh Scarce Blue-tails that I have seen have dots or commas. It would be of interest to know if there was a higher incidence of 'square brackets' in the other isolated, more easterly, colonies. The Scarce "Blue-tip" as the Irish call it is shown with square brackets in "Irelands Dragonflies"[3], and again it has square brackets in the Dragonflies of Hampshire[4].

The colour of the thorax changes from a pale straw colour to green and then finally blue as the damselfly acquires full maturity.

Maturing females undergo an even more dramatic colour change because as they mature they pass through what is called an *aurantiaca* stage when they are bright orange. A mature female is very dark, almost black above, and a bronzey green below. The lower sides of the female thorax are a striking, apple green.

My attention was first drawn to the Scarce Blue-tails when I found the Herefordshire colony while they were flying in the 'wheel position'. The underside of the female, which is exposed in this position seemed to be remarkably light compared with the Blue-tailed Damselflies in the same position. If this feature, which I have not read about elsewhere, helps others to discover another colony of these inconspicuous damselflies I shall feel it was worth mentioning. On the day I discovered my colony, Scarce Blue-tailed Damselflies were far from my thoughts. Long ago I had given up searching for them in the runnels that run down from the Black Mountains into the Olchon Valley, and in the gravel pits at Wellington, Aymestrey and Mathon, and indeed, I looked for them at Stretton Sugwas in the early 1990s. So the lighter underside of the female abdomen proved to be a valuable alert.

Another feature which can catch the eye is the tiny oval, two tone pterostigma. Both the "blue-tailed damselflies" have half black, half white pterostigmas, but they are different in size. The Blue-tail has a larger, more elongated pterostigma, whereas that of the Scarce Blue-tail is smaller and rounder. Ironically, although smaller, it is more conspicuous on the Scarce Blue-tail; the white seems more pearly and contrasts more with the black.

Knowing the habitat can be the best way to find Scarce Blue-tails. Having seen them in Pembrokeshire at Menybridd I had a picture in my mind of the more westerly Welsh type of habitat; then while looking for plants at Tregaron Bog in central west Wales, I came to a spot which screamed out 'Scarce Blue-tailed Damselfly', but at first sight there was not an insect to be seen of any description, and then movement : a thin shadow close to the water surface, lost, then seen again, and then another and eventually I realised that the right habitat, in the right part of the country had allowed me to find Scarce Blue-tailed Damselflies. Without recognising the habitat 'signature' I would not have found them. Colonies are often small, sparsely populated and scarce, this is not an insect that is easy to find!

Behaviour

Scarce Blue-tails stay close to the water surface, presumably for shelter, and appear to fly slowly between the stems of rushes and grasses. They rarely fly for long without settling, normally holding a vertical stem by their feet and projecting horizontally from it. With close focusing x10 binoculars it is easy to see the diagnostic abdominal tail markings when they are settled in this position.

Males and females fly about in this manner and the more difficult task of identifying the females is greatly simplified when a courting male 'latches' on. In early June almost half the

3   Nelson B. and Thomson R. 2004
4   Taverner J., Cham S., Hold A. e tal. 2004

LC

Immature female Scarce Blue-tail (aurantiaca phase).

LC

Large Red Damselfly – male attempting to mate with Scarce Blue-tailed – female (aurantiaca phase).

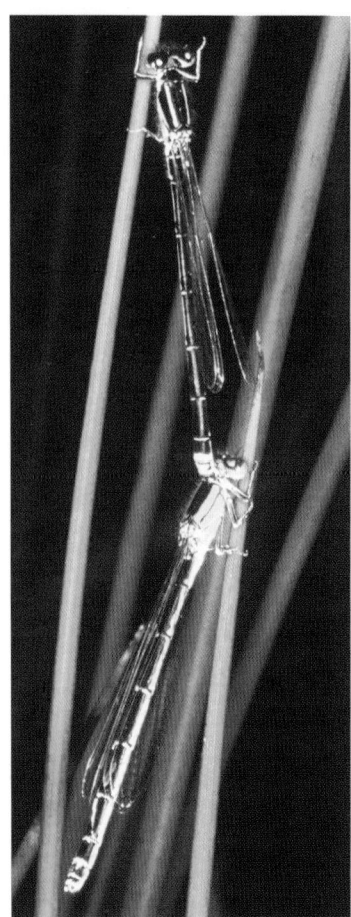

A pair of Scarce Blue-tails in tandem – note colour of mature female

Scarce Blue-tails in the colony (about 30 in total) are joined in 'tandem'.

While photographing the colony at Stretton Sugwas in early June 2002 with Les Clarke we noticed a most unusual pairing. Intra-specific pairings in damselflies are unusual, possibly because the male anal claspers of one species are not designed to "fit" the neck of a female of a different species. On the rare occasions when I have witnessed a mis-match it has been between two very similar species of blue damselflies and it has been a fleeting liaison. On this occasion a male Large Red Damselfly grabbed and stayed coupled with an *'aurantiaca'* phase female Scarce Blue-tail for at least five minutes *(see lower picture on opposite page)*. The female Scarce Blue-tail did not meekly consent to this assault. Not only was she the wrong species but she was 'only a girl' and not yet mature enough for such goings on! She struggled violently, writhing, twisting and pulling away from the Large Red. After brief pauses, which allowed photo opportunities, the struggle continued until they eventually broke apart. She flew off showing no 'outward' signs of harm.

Why did the Large Red grab her? I can only conjecture that he mistook the immature orange phase of the Scarce Blue-tail for the somewhat metallic bronzed female of his own species. At no time did he bring his legs or mouth parts near her suggesting he might have viewed her as prey.

Although Scarce Blue-tails are weak fliers and appear to live low amongst the sparse vegetation of their often restricted habitat, they are renowned for their powers of dispersal – they are colonists at newly created habitats. On occasions they achieve this by flying vertically, perhaps aided by thermals, until they can be blown by the wind. On 31st May 2000 there were many freshly emerged tenerals in the colony and several *aurantiaca* phase females. There was a strong south westerly breeze and many individuals were being blown out of the limited confines of the flush: a sizeable number would never become acquainted with the 'ancestral home'.

Amongst dragonflies and damselflies the Scarce Blue-tail is unusual in so far as it completes its life cycle within a few months. This rapid development is aided by the peculiarities of its habitat: shallow water which can warm up quickly in the sun so long as the vegetation is sparse or grazed low, a gentle flow helping to prevent freezing which could prove fatal in very shallow water and very soft substrate to provide nutrients and cover.

The soft mud of the flush at Stretton Sugwas Gravel Pit is so soft and deep in places I have lost a wellington boot on one occasion. On another, water and foul smelling, oozing mud poured into both boots and left me with a most uncomfortable journey home, but not dispirited! I have felt hugely privileged to be able to study this rare insect in Herefordshire.

The Blue-tailed Damselfly *Ischnura elegans*

Blue-tail – male

Flight Period
Most commonly seen during the second half of May and throughout June, July and August.

Status

National
Very common throughout all of lowland Britain and Ireland.

Herefordshire – 29/30
Widespread and very common. There are more records on the data base for the Blue-tailed Damselfly than any other species. However, although it is recorded from more sites than the other two common blue damselflies (Common Blue and Azure) it does not normally occur in such prolific numbers.

Blue-Tailed Damselfly
Ischnura elegans

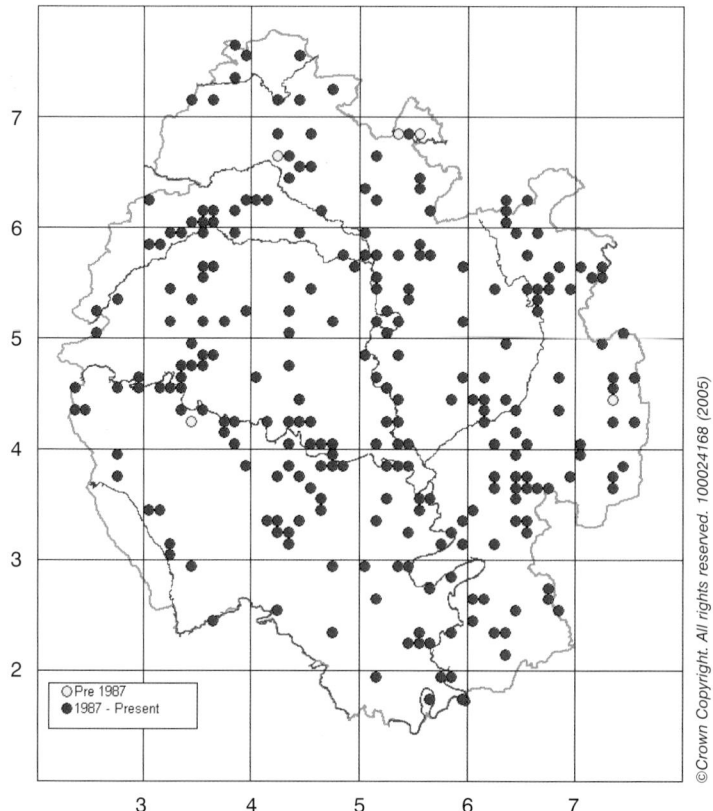

Legend:
- ○ Pre 1987
- ● 1987 - Present

Habitat

It has a catholic taste in breeding sites which can include lakes, ponds, ditches, garden ponds, canals and slow flowing streams and rivers. I have observed Blue-tails to be more numerous beside streams in July and August than earlier in the season – River Frome 5/7/03, River Lugg at Shelwick Green 19/7/04.

It is more tolerant of pollution than any of the other Dragonfly species. This is best illustrated by its presence on farm ponds that appear to consist largely of run-off from manure heaps and animal sheds. Typically such ponds, choked with Float Grass (*glycenia sp.*), are home to a small population of Blue-tails with no other species of Dragonfly in sight, but at many of these sites breeding is extremely unlikely. I would also suggest that many more such sites exist than I have investigated, so the distribution map for the Blue-tailed Damselfly is almost certainly missing many dots.

Description

A small damselfly with a shiny black abdomen except for segment eight. This eighth segment in the male twinkles clear blue and makes identification easy. The male also has thin blue antehumeral stripes and blue eye-spots.

The female is much more variable and exhibits five colour forms, two immature and three mature:

- f. *violacea*

  Immature
  antehumeral stripes – violet, sides of thorax – violet, eye-spots – violet, segment eight – blue
  (Matures into the normal form f. *infuscans*)

- f. *rufescens*

  Immature
  thorax - rose-pink, no antehumeral stripes just a black line, eye-spots – rose-pink, segment eight – blue
  (Matures into f. *rufescens – obsoleta*)
  NB Immatures take just over a week to mature

- Andromorph form

  Mature
  The 'normal form' with the thorax coloured the same as the male but lacking the bright blue abdominal segment eight

- f. *infuscans*

  Mature
  Sides of the thorax and antehumeral stripes - green, yellowish or brown, eye-spots olive - green to blue, segment eight – brown to almost black

- f. *rufescens-obsoleta*

  Mature
  No black antehumeral stripes, thorax – yellowish-brown to straw coloured, eye-spots – straw coloured, segment eight – brown

This all seems very complicated, but the salient points are that there are a variety of female forms so one must not imagine one is discovering new species. Some of the colour forms are very attractive and they all occur commonly in Herefordshire.

At the Moody Farm fishing lake near Longtown (SO3230) on 6th July 2003, I saw all five forms of female Blue-tail Damselfly and some were brighter green, violet or pink than others.

Behaviour

They appear to be less energetic than most other species. I tend to find them resting, flattened onto water-side vegetation where they would be hard to spot if it was not for their tell-tale blue tails. They do not seem to fly in tandem as often as other species, probably because the female egg lays alone.

Where there are many together, cannibalism has been recorded. I have not observed this but I have noticed that they are quite aggressive and do seem to attack other species of damselfly. With damselflies it is sometimes difficult to distinguish between courtship and warfare and males from one species sometimes attempt to mate with females from another species *(see note under Scarce Blue-tailed Damselfly)*.

LC

Form *rufescens*

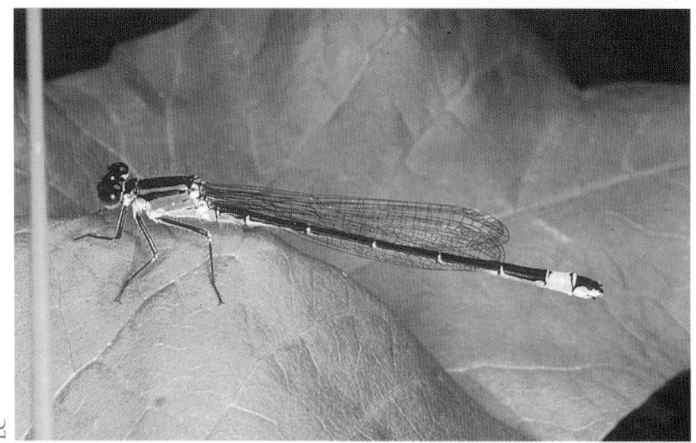

LC

Form *violacea*

LC

Form *infuscans*

The Hawkers

The Hawkers are large dragonflies that hunt on the wing, tirelessly patrolling their 'patch'. When at rest they hang in a perpendicular position unlike the shorter darters, skimmers and chasers that perch horizontally. On the Herefordshire list there are six species of hawker:

The Hairy Dragonfly	*Brachytron pratense*
Common Hawker	*Aeshna juncea*
Migrant Hawker	*Aeshna mixta*
Southern Hawker	*Aeshna cyanea*
Brown Hawker	*Aeshna grandis*
Emperor Dragonfly	*Anax imperator*

Brown Hawker – female.

The Common Hawker *Aeshna juncea*

Flight Period
Nationally it is most likely to occur from July to September – a high summer/autumn species. The Herefordshire records have all been in August and September.

Status

National
A very common species in the upland areas of north and west Britain including most of Wales, Scotland and northern parts of Ireland. Elsewhere it is extremely local.

Herefordshire – 5/30
The Common Hawker is far from common; I have seen it in Herefordshire on less than a dozen occasions, but I would speculate that it is under recorded in the west of Herefordshire.

I have only observed it ovipositing at one site – Peelers Pool (SO4772), where I also suspect Black Darter is breeding, but I expect there are other suitable breeding pools in the extreme west of Herefordshire. Martin Peer's account of 'The Dragonflies of Radnorshire'[1] records the Common Hawker in every Radnorshire 10km square except SO 13, 24 and 36.

Habitat
Common Hawkers prefer acidic water and are commonly found on moorland pools and bogs. The Irish call it the Moorland Hawker. In keeping with the other species in the Aeshna genus it can frequently be found away from breeding habitat hawking along streams and in woodland rides and clearings.

Description
The pattern on the abdomen of the mature male of this species is blue spots alternating with yellow triangles on a brown background; on the female the spots are green. Immature males have yellow spots and there is a blue spotted form of the female, so care must be taken, and other features must be observed to guarantee identification. Perhaps the key characteristic of both sexes is the bright yellow costa on all wings, but this is not always an easy field characteristic to observe.

The two yellow antehumeral stripes on the male are narrow but distinctive. They are much broader on Southern Hawker and appear to be more like dots on the Migrant Hawker. There are two diagonal yellow stripes on the sides of the thorax.

Even though the Migrant Hawker is smaller, it is the species most likely to be confused with Common Hawker. The size and the antehumeral stripes help, but I have not recorded it without seeing the yellow costa.

Behaviour
Territorial males at breeding ponds fly low over the water exploring the nooks and crannies of the bank but not flying amongst vegetation in the way of the Hairy Dragonfly

---

1   Peers M. (1985)

Common Hawker
Aeshna juncea

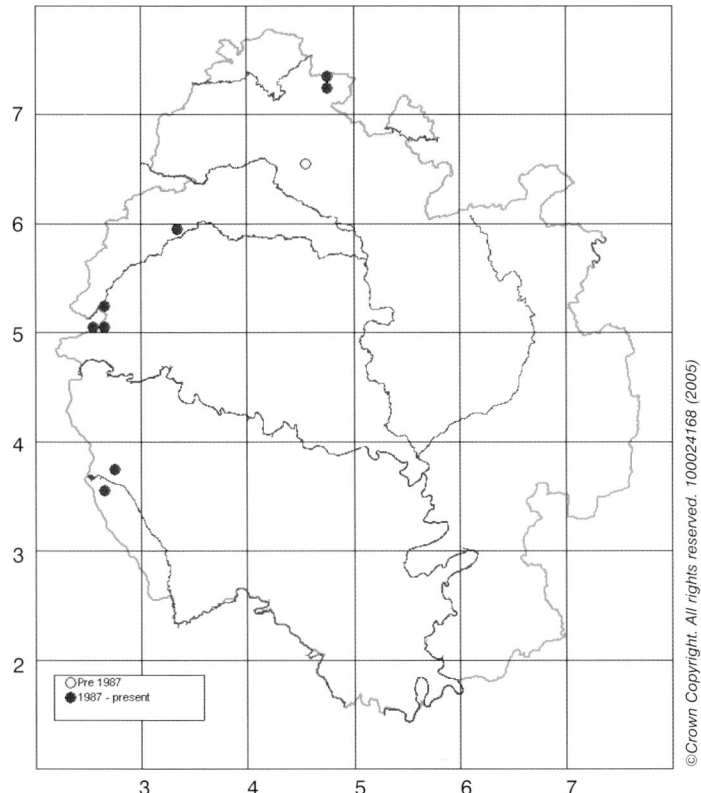

and the Migrant Hawker. Nor does the fly a regular beat like the Emperor. I watched a male methodically working it's way round the edges of Peeler's Pool and then veering across the pool, grabbing a female and flying up into the trees with her as another jealous male buzzed and snapped at them.

Common Hawkers frequently fly considerable distances from their breeding pools to hunt. They can be found hawking along woodland edges and hedge-lined roads and tracks. Close to Herefordshire's border with Radnorshire (Powys) I have watched them hunting in this way and then moving up (probably following prey) into the tree canopy where they would have remained undetected if I had not seen them at a lower level first.

The Migrant Hawker *Aeshna mixta*

Flight Period

This late emerging dragonfly is on the wing from the end of July until late October, but is most likely to be seen in the second half of August, September and most of October.

Status

National

A common, late summer dragonfly across most of southern England, the Midlands and the coastal fringe of south Wales. Very recently (2000) established in south east Ireland. As it's name suggests the Migrant Hawker was first known only as a migrant in this country, but by the mid 20th Century there was proof of breeding and now the well established British population is 'topped-up' by regular waves of immigrants.

Herefordshire – 26/30

There were no previous Herefordshire records for this hawker before mine on 20th September 1986 at Mathon Gravel Pit (SO7344), but it is likely that it had colonised parts of the county several years before this. Breeding was first confirmed in neighbouring Gloucestershire[1] in 1976 and Migrant Hawker was first recorded in our eastern neighbour – Worcestershire in 1978.[2] It is now widespread and common in the county with very large numbers present at some sites – Mathon Gravel Pit 20+ (27-09-91), Docklow Fishing Pools (SO5557) 20+ (14-09-97) Stretton Sugwas Gravel Pit (SO4442) 30+ (29-09-02).

LC

Migrant Hawker male. Note the almost non-existent antehumeral stripes.

Habitat

The Migrant Hawker can be found by most sunny, unpolluted areas of standing water except for very small garden ponds, which the Southern Hawker finds attractive. They do not breed in acidic pools, but this type of habitat is virtually non-existent in Herefordshire. I would suggest they prefer a well-developed fringe of marginal vegetation such as Reedmace *Typha sp.* as a site for ovipositing.

---

1   Holland S. (1991)
2   Averill M. (1996)

Migrant Hawker
Aeshna mixta

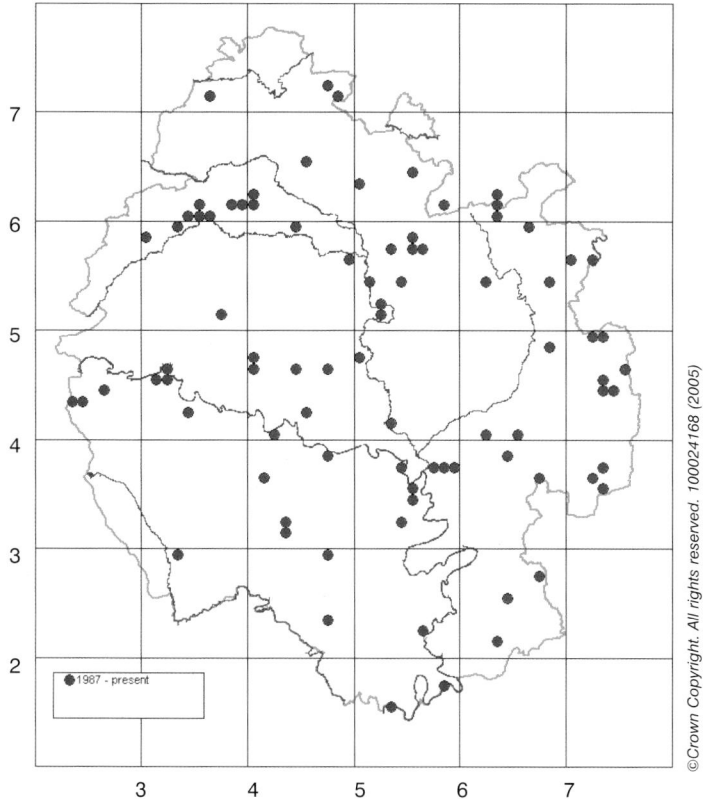

Description

The Migrant Hawker is smaller than the Southern and Common Hawkers, appearing very dark in flight. The dark-brown abdomen has a distinctive narrow yellow triangle on segment two and paired small blue spots on all the other segments. The antehumeral stripes are either absent or reduced to dots and the sides of the thorax are brown with two diagonal yellow stripes. In the female the paired spots on each of the segments of the abdomen are yellow or yellow-green. The narrow yellow triangle at the top of the abdomen is an important diagnostic feature in the female as well as the male.

I have found that a most valuable aid to identification of the Migrant Hawker is a bright light-blue patch on the side and beneath the second segment of the abdomen, which is conspicuous when in flight *(see photo on the next page)*.

Behaviour

Much is written about large groups of Migrant Hawkers hunting away from water at the woodland edge or in sheltered clearings, I have never recorded any such behaviour in Herefordshire. As I have written under 'Status' I have recorded quite remarkable concentrations of this species around suitable breeding pools, but I would speculate that gatherings (I'm not sure of the collective noun for dragonflies) away from water are a phenomenon of recently arrived migrants. In Herefordshire it is close to the extremity of its range and remote from points of arrival from the continent. If the majority of Herefordshire Migrant Hawkers are part of a resident British population, which is gradually colonising further north and west, it might explain why 'gang meetings' are not observed in our county. When many of them are flying together in the same area it is interesting to note that clashes and skirmishes are few. Probably one would not expect fiercely territorial behaviour from a species which has a powerful drive to disperse and migrate in 'flocks'.

None of the other Herefordshire hawkers hover in the same way as a Migrant Hawker. It remains in the same spot whirring its wings, transfixed in mid-air, for much longer than any other dragonfly I have seen. When it does this the blue spot at the base of the abdomen is clearly apparent. It is wonderful to focus binoculars on it when it hovers in this way; it also provides an excellent opportunity for an ambitious photographer.

Photographs in books of dragonflies in flight are unusual, but when they do occur it is invariably the Migrant Hawker which features.

One is often first aware of a female by the loud rapid rustling of her wings amongst the tall marginal vegetation as she oviposits alone. On 30th August 1998 at Staunton Green (SO3660) I made intimate observations of a Migrant Hawker ovipositing into Bur-reed – *Sparganium erectum.* '

"About 30 cm above the water level, with legs wide apart and abdomen tip curled round to face the stem the female Migrant Hawker worked her way round the stem slowly maintaining the same level above the water. This lasted at least 10 minutes – I stopped watching before she had finished – intermittent wing rustling betrayed her position."

In Herefordshire more Migrant Hawkers, male and female, are encountered well away from water, than any other species of hawker and most years they even stay on the wing later into the season than the Southern Hawker. Autumn reports of a dragonfly in the garden, often where there is no pond, flying beside hedges and round and between small trees, is most likely to be the Migrant Hawker.

Migrant Hawker hovering.

The Southern Hawker *Aeshna cyanea*

Female Southern Hawker. Note the broad antehumeral stripes and undivided bands on segments 8 and 9 of her abdomen

Flight Period

The Southern Hawker emerges in late June and stays on the wing until early November[1] but it is most abundant from the second week of July to early October

Status

National

Widespread and common over almost all of England and Wales. There are small, recently established, isolated colonies in Scotland, but it is absent from Ireland.

Herefordshire – 29/30

The Southern Hawker is common and widespread. The most commonly seen dragonfly at garden ponds especially in high summer. It is most frequently reported to me by members of the public who love their garden pond, but have only a generalised interest in wildlife.

---

1 I have received November records for this species from Roger Maskew at Stoke Bliss (SO6463) on the Herefordshire/Worcestershire border but *just* in Worcestershire.

Southern Hawker
Aeshna cyanea

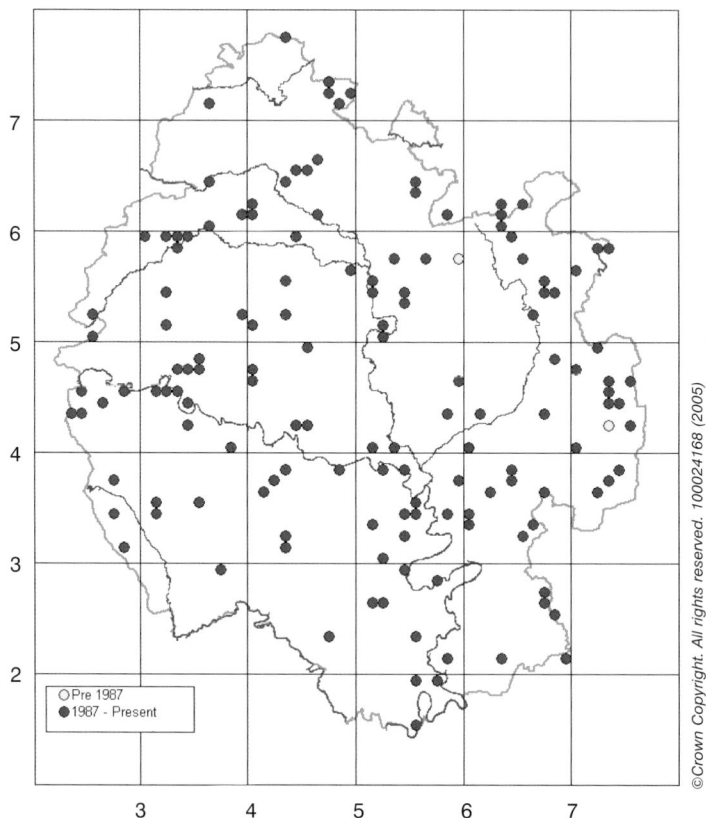

Legend:
○ Pre 1987
● 1987 - Present

Habitat

Almost all sunny, non-acidic ponds, lakes and canals are potential breeding sites for this dragonfly. They do not seem to mind how small the pond is – garden ponds the size of a horse-trough are often used. I have received reports from astonished and fascinated pond owners who have observed 10's of Southern Hawkers coming off their bath sized ornamental pond.

It is probably their intolerance of acidic conditions rather then climatic constraints which accounts for its absence from north Wales, but climate is most likely to be the overriding factor inhibiting its colonisation of Scotland and Ireland[1].

Description

The male Southern Hawker attracts initial attention as a large dark brown, green and blue dragonfly and the female lacks the blue. The ground colour is dark brown and the

---

1   Merritt R. et al. 1996

bright apple green is in the form of pairs of spots on segments one to seven on the top of the abdomen, two large sausage shaped antehumeral stripes and side stripes on the thorax. There are blue side spots along the length of the male abdomen and there are two very conspicuous blue bars (not spots) on the last two abdominal segments.

Immatures of both sexes have a lighter brown background and pale yellow markings. I have twice received reports of Golden-ringed Dragonflies from garden ponds in Hereford and have guessed that the observer has been confused by a recently emerged Southern Hawker.

I have once seen a rare 'blue' form of the Southern Hawker in Herefordshire. This is a recognised form of the male where all green markings on the abdomen are replaced by blue. The green sides to the thorax and the green antehumeral stripes were unchanged. There was no risk of mis-identification because the blue on the 'tail' was in the form of bands not divided into spots and the antehumeral stripes were broad and very conspicuous.

These are the two diagnostic features of Southern Hawker. In flight the blue "bars" on segments 9 and 10, make this dragonfly look as if it has a blue tail and the broad antehumeral stripes (shoulder stripes) are described by some as 'headlights'. They appear as such when it is flying directly towards you – something that this dragonfly often does!

Behaviour

There are several reasons why the Southern Hawker is the most widely reported dragonfly by the general public: one is its constant quest for new breeding sites and feeding

Southern Hawker egg laying into the moss on the edge of a dry bird-bath

87

grounds means that it is often encountered far from water, another is its attraction to even the smallest garden pond for breeding. I have received a photograph of a female attempting to oviposit in the mossy edge of a bird bath in Hereford *(see previous page)*. On another occasion the Herefordshire Nature Trust passed on to me the telephone number of a lady living near Leominster who had phoned them because she was concerned by the presence of a large green and brown dragonfly in her lounge and conservatory. When I contacted her she explained that she had managed to guide it out through a window, only for it to have returned half an hour later. She described to me how it was curling its abdomen underneath it as if trying to 'sting' the top of her curtains. We concluded that for some bizarre reason it was trying to oviposit in the curtain ruflette – they were patterned green and blue!

This rather eccentrically behaved dragonfly not only enjoys our gardens but it also regards people with a curious fascination. Fishermen frequently recount how a large blue and green dragonfly has hovered only a couple of feet in front of them staring straight at them. This behaviour is repeated for almost every pool side visitor and it is difficult to understand why the Southern Hawker does it. I have wondered if it sees people simply as large mammals, whether it does the same for cows and horses and it views us as an attraction for flies. It is checking us out for a buzz of insects and is probably puzzled and disappointed that our cleaner habits mean we do not source the meal that a cow most likely does.

When hunting, it will fly until late in the day and in relatively inclement weather. On 5th August 1997 I made the following note about two Southern Hawkers as I walked down the track which approaches Mathon Gravel Pit from the west.

> *'The last three days have been wet, windy and cool. This evening at 8.00pm not raining but cold and windy I had two Southern Hawker males flying up and down the track. The track is very sheltered with a bank on one side and high hedges on both. The dragonflies flew up and down weaving from side to side and at times flashing up to the hedge top for an instant before resuming their patrolling flight which was at a constant knee-height.'*

On 29th August 1998 (one year later) a cool evening at 7.30pm after a bright sunny day I recorded two Southern Hawkers behaving in exactly the same way in exactly the same spot.

Although I did not see them catch anything it is likely they were feeding on gnats. However, they will catch much larger prey. They have been known to catch darter dragonflies, and I have observed one catch a Small White Butterfly. It flew with it into the top of a pool side Alder and soon after I saw the wings floating down.

I have noted that many pools in high summer – mid-July/early August have no Southern Hawkers, but plenty of Emperors. Then as Emperors start to 'fade' towards the end of August and throughout September, Southern Hawkers appear in good numbers. I wondered if this was because the Emperors drove the Southern Hawkers off the pools, but it is more likely that the Southern Hawkers emerge and hunt away from the breeding territory until fully mature and then return to the pools to breed just as the Emperors are coming to the end of their flight period.

During the period of time (second half of August) when both species are on the same pools the Emperor does seem to be the more dominant species – even more powerful in flight and slightly larger – Southern Hawkers come off second best.

While the males are battling it out over the pond the females are unobtrusively working their way round the pool margins probing with their ovipositors into mossy edges, soft mud, rotten wood or submerged water-weeds. She will continue round the shore in this manner oblivious to fishermen or the casual observer passing within a few feet of them.

She will oviposit in moss or damp mud well above the waterline, then when the winter rains fill the pond her eggs are best placed to hatch because the marginal water warms quickest where it is shallow.

Despite the random inappropriate choice of sites to deposit eggs, female Southern Hawkers must normally make wise choices for their off-spring because this is a common, widespread and very successful insect. At some pools over a thousand exuviae have been counted and even tiny garden ponds can host over a hundred.

PGG

Southern Hawker – male

The Brown Hawker *Aeshna grandis*

A worn Brown Hawker – male.

Flight Period

The Brown Hawker is most likely to be seen between mid-July and early September.

There is an unconfirmed record for the 4th of June 1998 which is an exceptionally early date (the next earliest record is 19-07-89) made by Dr Michael Harper in a field next to his home just south of Ledbury. He is a nationally renowned and highly respected lepidopterist, but has no specialist knowledge of Dragonflies. However, it is difficult to confuse Brown Hawker with any other species and Michael Harper had excellent views as he watched it eat a large green shield-bug which he identified as *Palomena prasina*.

Status

National
Common throughout most of England, especially in the lowlands of the midlands and the southeast. Absent from the southwest of England, most of Wales and Scotland, but widespread and common in Ireland.

Herefordshire – 15/30
Regularly seen and almost undoubtedly breeding at many sites in the east and north of the county. Far less frequently encountered throughout the rest of the county with only one unconfirmed record from southwest Herefordshire[1].

---

1   The head gardener on the Whitfield Estate claimed to have seen this distinctive dragonfly on one of the large pools on the estate, but he could not give me a date – he was not even sure of the year.

Brown Hawker
Aeshna grandis

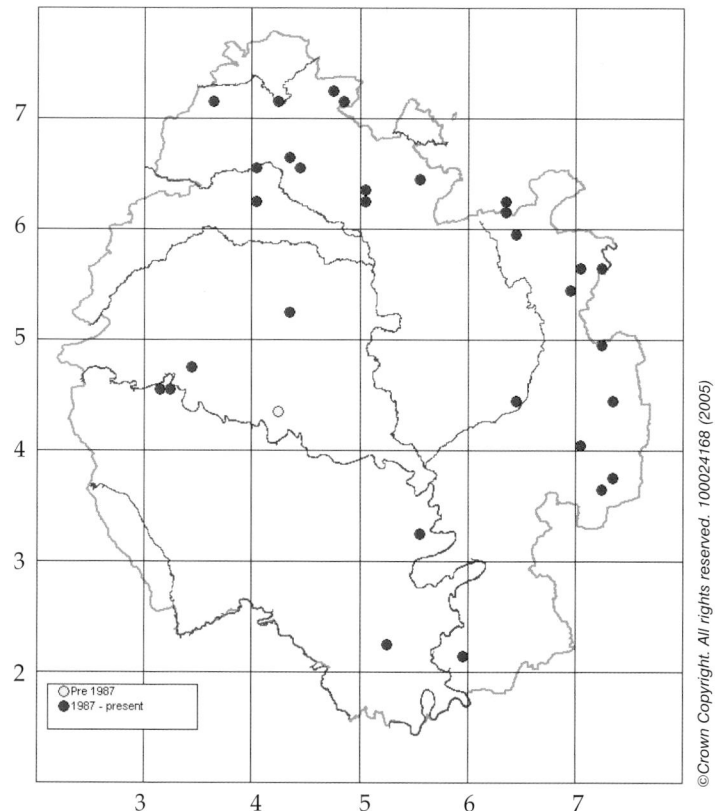

Legend: ○ Pre 1987　● 1987 - present

It would seem reasonable to conclude that Herefordshire is the western boundary of the Brown Hawker's range in England and Wales. The distribution map for Worcestershire[2] shows a slightly less concentrated distribution of records in the west. I am not aware of any records for Brown Hawker from Radnorshire.[3]

It appears to be extending its range south and westwards, gradually colonising the county. When Parker[4] carried out his, admittedly limited, one year survey he did not record Brown Hawker. It is such a conspicuous insect I can only assume it was either absent or rare in 1977. Ever since I have been recording however, they have been much in evidence on

---

2　Averill M. 1996
3　Peers M. 1985
4　Parker D.M. 1978

several pools in the extreme north east of Herefordshire: Whitbourne Hall Lake (SO7256). Mathon Gravel Pit (SO7344), Netherwood (SO6361). Grittlesend Pools (SO7249). Lawn Pool – Brockhampton (SO6954).

But in recent years (mostly since the turn of the century) it has turned up in areas where I have not seen it previously – further to the south and west: Shobdon Pools (SO4062) – 2003, Weston Farm Pool (SO3245) – 2004, Llangarron (SO5222) – 2005.

Habitat

Most literature suggests that the Brown Hawker has a very catholic taste for breeding habitat and can be found on ponds, canals, lakes or slow flowing rivers, and my experience of them in Worcestershire would bear this out. However, in Herefordshire they seem to only choose pools that have tall stands of trees on at least one side. In Worcestershire I have seen them in large numbers over open pools on golf courses, but in Herefordshire there are always tall trees at the water edge or else nearby. It is interesting to note that Nelson and Thompson[5], when describing the Irish habitat for the Brown Hawker (or Amber-winged Hawker as it is called in Ireland), also make reference to this dragonfly's preference for 'small lakes and fens with many trees and bushes'. There are several pools in the south of the county that appear to be perfect for Brown Hawkers, but where none have been recorded. I believe it is only a matter of time before they turn up on these pools as well.

Description

Apart from the Norfolk Hawker, which has never been seen anywhere near this county, there is no other species of dragonfly which one could confuse with The Brown Hawker. A larger brown-bodied dragonfly with broad amber tinted wings – always an exciting sight for me!

Males and females only differ slightly in body shape and detailed pattern colouring. The body of the male has a slight waisting of segment two and three: without this the female appears to be more robust. There are blue spots along the sides of the abdomen (yellow in the female) and two blue spots that are so close together they almost form a thin ring on the top of segment two. The delight is in the detail! These fine blue markings on the brown background are wonderfully colour co-ordinated with the lemon yellow diagonal stripes on the thorax. The Brown Hawker is a splendid sight but unfortunately ageing and somewhat worn specimens are the ones that are most often seen. This is because by the time they return to their pools to hold territory and breed, which is when they are most easily observed, they bear the scars and tears from hawking high in the trees. Furthermore a tear in a Brown Hawker's brown wing is more apparent than in most other species that have clear wings.

Behaviour

Like all the other hawkers it flies back and forth, over pond or lake patrolling its patch, but it can also be seen hunting along the edges of woods where they border the lake or waterside rows of alders. They fly high up near the tree tops and because of the colour of their wings one can continue to observe them from a considerable distance, especially through binoculars. Brown Hawkers glide more than other dragonflies and hover less. At times their glide is reminiscent of a tropical butterfly. They are less often seen when at rest because their brown appearance provides good camouflage and they tend to settle high up in the trees.

---

5   Nelson B. and Thompson R. 2004

The Emperor Dragonfly *Anax imperator*

Emperor – male

Flight Period

The Emperor flies from late May to early September but is most likely to be seen during June, July and August

Status

National

Widespread and common in southern England, the Midlands and south Wales. The Emperor avoids upland areas but otherwise is expanding its range rapidly. For instance, breeding was first confirmed from Cheshire as recently as 1993[1], it has now continued to colonise parts of northern England and since the turn of the century has established a foothold in southeast Ireland and a couple of isolated colonies in Scotland.

Herefordshire – 29/30

Like the Migrant Hawker and the Ruddy Darter the Emperor has recently colonised Herefordshire, and it has made a very good job of it! Whenever I approach a pond or lake

---

1 Merritt R.et al. 1996

Emperor Dragonfly
Anax imperator

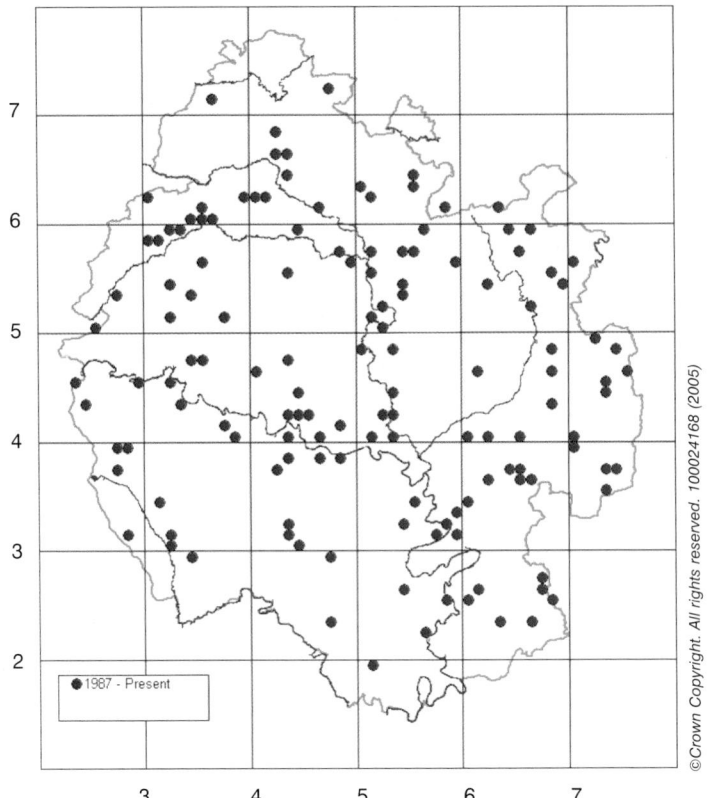

in the summer months for the first time I expect to see an Emperor flying over it and I am rarely disappointed, and at several pools there appears to be a re-enactment of the Battle of Britain as males joust for territory.

Parker (1978) listed three records for Herefordshire; Peers (1985) just two for Radnorshire; Averill reported only a handful for Worcestershire prior to 1984 and Holland (1991) knew the species from just three hectads before 1976 in Gloucestershire but from twenty-seven by 1991.

Apart from the acidic upland waters of Radnorshire it is safe to assume that it is now widespread and common in all neighbouring counties. The complete colonisation of Herefordshire and its region by the Emporer has been accomplished in twenty five years.

Habitat

Ponds and lakes with tall marginal vegetation and some pondweed or similar floating vegetation make excellent breeding and hunting grounds for the Emperor.

However, it can be found patrolling quite recently created pools. It is an early colonist and has benefited from the post war proliferation of gravel pits. On 27th June 1993 I estimated there were over fifty Emperors at Mathon Gravel Pit. At a recently created golf course at The Grove, just south of Leominster, five pools varying in size from three or four metres in diameter to over twenty have been created. Within a year of being filled and even before the course was open to the public in 2004, Emperors were flying over four of them.

Unlike the Southern Hawker the Emperor is not commonly found on garden ponds unless they are considerably larger than the average or close to other larger pools.

On three occasions I have recorded the Emperor holding territory on the Wye and once on a stretch of the Lugg. On the Wye records extend as far upstream as Winforton (SO2945) – 2001, to Caplar (SO5832) – 1996 and downstream as far as Glewstone (SO5622) – 2003. An Emperor was patrolling a quiet stretch of the Lugg near Gilbert's Farm (SO4661) in 1995. On all these occasions it patrolled a stretch of river 25-50 metres long.

Description

The Emperor is Britain's largest dragonfly, and mature males can look stunning: their light green thorax contrasts with the slightly tapered enamel-blue abdomen. It does not have an intricate pattern of markings on the abdomen like the other hawkers, but it is distinguished by a central black stripe. The black line barely divides the first two thickened segments of the abdomen and this impresses as a conspicuous clear blue patch behind the base of the wings. The otherwise clear wings have a yellow costa.

The female is shorter and less eye catching as the bright blue of the male is replaced by a rather dull green. The guide books warn that male coloured blue females sometimes occur. I have never seen one in Herefordshire.

The male can be safely identified in flight even when the light conditions do not allow a clear view of its remarkable colouring, because it flies in a bowed fashion holding its abdomen with the end curved down.

Behaviour

It is a powerful flyer and a very aggressive territorial dragonfly. I have watched them tirelessly patrolling their territory without stopping to rest for twenty minutes. More typically they will fly for about five minutes, 'hang up' briefly, maybe to eat a larger prey item, then continue on patrol. Like all the hawkers they hang vertically, normally from vegetation, and it is at such moments one has the chance for a more detailed look. Great care is needed to get close enough for a good photograph because it is a wary dragonfly and certainly does not share the Southern Hawkers predisposition for humans.

Unlike many other dragonflies the Emperor does not confine itself to the margins of larger pools which, perhaps, explains its liking for more extensive bodies of water. It flies at head height or higher above the water and can eat small prey on the wing, which is convenient when some distance away from a suitable resting place. When flying at this steady level it will shoot up high after prey, or flash to one side or the other with awe-inspiring manoeuvrability before resuming its previous flight path.

Clashes with others of the same species are frequent, dramatic and often prolonged, but again, after disengagement the territorial patrol is resumed. My first encounter with Emperors in Herefordshire was on the 27th June 1986 at Mathon Gravel Pit: three males were locked in furious combat. At the time I compared the noise they made, as their wings repeatedly clashed to 'someone tearing the cellophane paper from a cigarette or chocolate box and screwing it up to throw it in the bin'.

It will chase away other large dragonflies: many pools in July and much of August are devoid of Southern Hawkers even where they are known to breed. Is this because they prefer to hunt away from water at this stage of their development? Or are they driven away from the breeding grounds by the more dominant and powerful Emperor? I wish I had studied the Herefordshire dragonflies before the advent of the Emperor: would the pools, where it now reigns supreme, have been dominated by Southern Hawkers?

It is so powerful it has been known to eat other dragonflies (Darters and even Chasers), but I have only seen them take Damselflies in Herefordshire. In June 1993 at Mathon Gravel Pit I watched two Emperors attack Large Red Damselflies, taking them away to eat at rest. Azure Damselflies were the commonest species flying and resting in the marginal vegetation in their hundreds, but the Emperors ignored them and concentrated on the few poor Large Reds that were there.

Roger Maskew watched one "have a go" at a Sand Martin at Holt Gravel Pit in neighbouring Worcestershire!

At Bodenham Lake in early August 1996 several Banded Demoiselles were mobbing an Emperor in the way small birds mob a Sparrow Hawk or crows mob a Buzzard. A clear indication of the 'pecking order' in the world of Dragonfly!

The shorter, slighly stouter and decidedly more dowdy looking female, oviposits without an attendant male, inserting her eggs into the stems of pondweeds just below the surface of the water. While perched on the edge of a Broad-leaved Pondweed *Potomageton natans* leaf, often well away from the edge of the pond with the tip of her abdomen curled under the water, the female Emperor is vulnerable to attack from birds or fish and is very well served by her less conspicuous colouring which blends in with water and the floating vegetation.

The Hairy Dragonfly *Brachytron pratense*

Flight Period

The Hairy Dragonfly has a very early flight season, emerging from the beginning to mid-May and usually finishing by the end of June just as one might expect to see the first emergence of some of the other hawkers. In Ireland it is more appropriately named the Spring Hawker. Of the two Herefordshire records one was described as 'early May 1978', and the other was on the 31st May 1977.

Status

National
Never common, the Hairy Dragonfly has a scattered distribution across much of southern England, with strongholds on the coastal marshes of Norfolk, Kent, Sussex and Somerset.

Hairy Dragonfly
Brachytron pratense

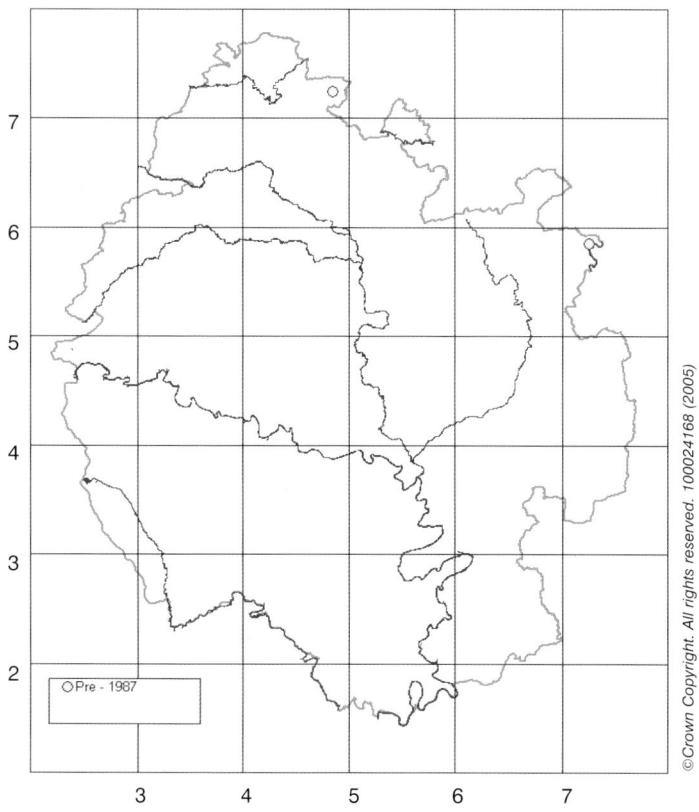

○ Pre - 1987

There are several coastal sites in south Wales and Anglesey, and one or two isolated sites elsewhere. It has also been found breeding in a few isolated sites in western Scotland. In Ireland it is widespread but uncommon. Following a national decline in post war years the Hairy Dragonfly is now showing signs of extending its range

Herefordshire - 2/30
I have never seen this dragonfly and would describe it as extinct in the county; if indeed it can be described as ever having had the status of a "Herefordshire insect". The two historical records which I will describe in greater detail later, almost certainly refer to passing individuals.

Habitat

In Britain this dragonfly is associated with fenland drainage channels, ditches and dykes but canals, ponds, lakes and even slow flowing rivers are used. Dense fringing vegetation such as *Phragmites, Typha, Schoenoplectus* seems to be an essential component at all sites.

Not only do such plants provide much needed shelter for this early season dragonfly, but they supply abundant floating detritus which is important for ovipositing females, and forms protection for the larvae.

The 1978 Herefordshire record was from a pool in the Mary Knoll Valley, very close to the Shropshire border. It was observed by Bob Kemp, an odontologist of international renown. The habitat seemed to me to be so atypical that I wrote to Bob and I enclose his reply:

Ist October 1996

Dear Peter

Re Brachytron pratense

Thank you for your letter of 27th Sept. You are correct in questioning the validity of my record of Brachytron from Mary Knoll Valley. You are not the first to do so!

The sighting was a single male patrolling the woodland ride close to what was then a fairly good pond (since drained I believe)[1] approx. half a mile from the road at the southern end of the valley. Although I never actually caught the specimen, I am in no doubt what so ever that it was Brachytron.

As regards unusual habitat. Over its range both nationally and in Europe I have encountered this insect in a variety of conditions. In Sweden for example it is fairly common on acidic lakes and pools associated with Sphagnum bog habitat. Indeed I have seen oviposition take place on floating, dead stems adjacent to the margin of a Scottish Lochan, slow-flowing rivers and calcarious fen have all been noted. What determines the scattered distribution of this insect is unknown but in general it does tend to favour mature, if not ancient, waterbodies and may well be a late coloniser. How well do they disperse?

Since the Mary Knoll Valley encounter, I have always expected to find Brachytron breeding within Shropshire. The most likely places would be the Meres and indeed a couple of unconfirmed sightings have been made. With the Hatchmere population not too far away this is quite possible.

---

1   The pool is still there – SO490728

I remember well John Day's record from Ankerdine Hill and also Dave Parker's[2] from Herefordshire but as to the authenticity of the recordings I would not like to say. My mention of Brachyton in the information leaflet was indeed due to John's record. Confusion with Gomphus is very possible.

I hope this sheds some light on the situation.

Best wishes and kind regards

Bob Kemp

The other Herefordshire record to which Bob Kemp refers in his letter was Dave Parker's[3] and he added a note to suggest that suitable breeding habitat was close by.

To infer that either record suggests breeding in Herefordshire is unsafe, but with the current indications of a range expansion I believe future records for the Hairy Dragonfly are quite probable.

Description

This is the smallest of all the hawkers, not much longer than the Club-tailed Dragonfly which is the only other similarly sized and shaped dragonfly on the wing in May and early June. The Hairy Dragonfly has small oval dots on each segment of the abdomen which are blue on the male and yellow on the female. Both sexes have a hairy thorax and the abdomen of the female is hairy as well, but this feature is not always apparent unless viewed at close range. They have a long, narrow, brown pterostigma and long anal appendages.

Behaviour

They are aggressively territorial and normally patrol at low levels quite close to the water surface. They only fly when the sun is shining, and at other times are resting in vegetation. One's attention is sometimes drawn to the ovipositing female, with attendant male, because of the noise of their wings beating against the vegetation. I have experienced this several times with Migrant Hawkers.

I have searched many seemingly suitable habitats for the Hairy Dragonfly and have searched the scenes of their previous visits to the county, but all to no avail. To be able to record this dragonfly in Herefordshire would cap twenty exciting years of surveying the county's Dragonflies!

---

2   John Day's record is one of just two Worcesterhire records. John and Dave's sightings were only 3 km apart and were made within a day of each other.

3   Parker D.M. 1978

The Club-tailed Dragonfly *Gomphus vulgatissimus*

PGG

A male Club-tail resting by the River Lugg with typical 'closed wings pose'.

Flight Period

Flying from the end of the first week in May but most abundant from mid- May until mid-June. The late July record in 1996 was most exceptional. In fact I have not been able to find publication of a later date for any year.

Status

National

A scarce dragonfly nationally, the Club-tail is confined to just seven river systems in England and Wales. These are the Tywi and Teifi in southwest Wales, the Thames and the Arun in south-central England, the Dee at the most northerly extent of its range and the Severn and Wye in the west Midlands.

Herefordshire – 9/30

The Club-tailed Dragonfly can be found in small numbers at most suitable points on the Wye as far upstream as Monnington (SO3544). It is breeding on the Lugg upstream as far as the Lugg Meadows, which is just seven or eight kilometres from its confluence with the Wye. It is also on the Teme in good numbers at the point where it forms the county boundary between Herefordshire and Worcestershire upstream a few kilometres from Knightwick.

Club-tailed Dragonfly
Gomphus vulgatissimus

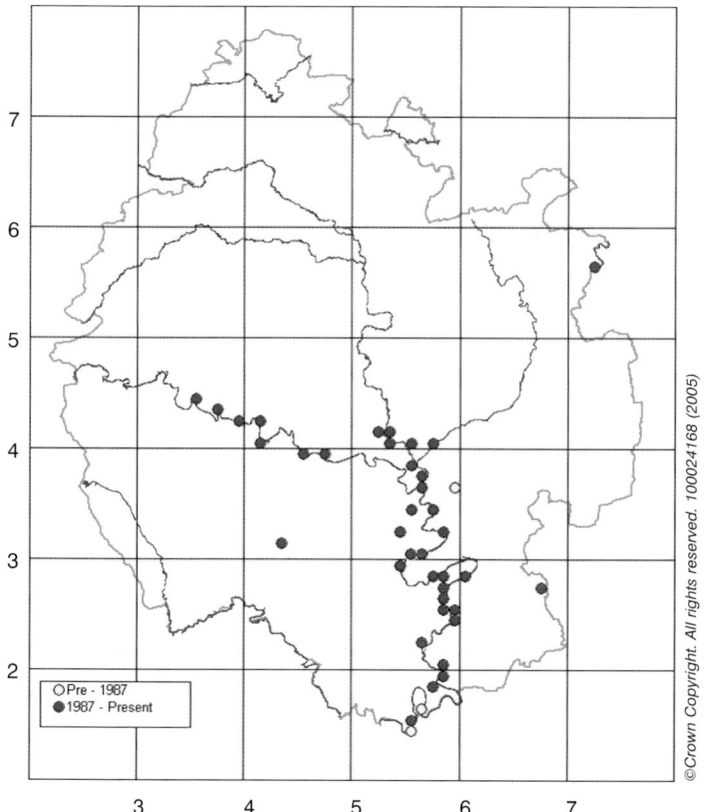

Legend:
○ Pre - 1987
● 1987 - Present

It is almost certain that the Club-tail has been under-recorded on the Wye, and the only way to get anything approaching an accurate census is to count exuviae along the river bank. Phyllis and Richard King are carrying out a controlled count along a stretch of the Wye at Hoarwithy under the direction of Mike Averill whose research into this species in Worcestershire has been widely acclaimed. In their first season of counting, 2004, from 15th May to 3rd June they had 32 exuviae (16 male and 16 female) along a 50m stretch. In 2005 during the same dates the number of exuviae rose to 41 (again with equal sexes).

This level of density surprised me because my general impression, from having frequently walked the banks of the Avon and Severn in Worcestershire, was that The Wye is less well populated with Club-tails than these two neighbouring Worcestershire rivers. However, Mike Averill informs us that our 2004 and 2005 counts are similar to the results from the Worcestershire rivers.

Habitat

The Club-tails require unpolluted, muddy bottomed rivers with a slow to moderate flow, and for the most part, with broad, thickly vegetated river banks. River meanders encourage the greatest concentrations of sediments and silt into which the larvae burrow. A hinterland of light fragmented woodland interspersed with "well-hedged" pasture and cereal fields might play some part in the preferred habitat of the Club-tail, but it is important to remember that environmental conditions for the aquatic phases of any dragonfly species will always be the predominant consideration.

Description

When walking beside the Wye or lower Lugg, during the second half of May, one is quite likely to encounter a medium-sized black dragonfly with extensive bright yellow patterning. This will be a recently emerged Club-tailed Dragonfly *(see photo on page 99)*. It will soon leave the riverside and one might see it take off and fly up and away. I have watched them through binoculars flying high and straight until they disappear as a distant dot.

If you are fortunate enough to see the same dragonfly, or one of its brothers or sisters, a few weeks later, perhaps hunting down a woodland ride it will have changed colour. Much of the yellow, especially on the male, changes to a pale, chalky green. It retains yellow markings along the sides of the abdomen and in the "tail". The female has more extensive yellow colouration along the sides of her abdomen. The eyes of a mature Club-tail are dull green.

Such encounters are relatively unusual so it is probably more helpful to concentrate in a little more detail on the immature Club-tails before they have left the riverbank, which is when this dragonfly is most often seen.

During the first few hours after emergence they are easiest to find and they are relatively easy to approach. They are very distinctly coloured yellow and black. For a short time after emergence they are very pale *(see picture on next page)*, but the dark areas soon become a shiny black, and the yellow darkens to a glossy buttercup colour. As their name suggests, the end of the abdomen, especially in the male, is swollen. The sides of the female's abdomen are straighter and this gives her a chunkier, more robust appearance. A good view from above of this dragonfly also allows one to observe the widely separated eyes: this feature is unique to the *"Gomphus"* genera (The *Gomphidae* of which the Club-tail is the only British member) - and immediately distinguishes the Club-tail from all other British dragonflies whose eyes are contiguous.

Even without a perfect view one should not confuse them with any other species. The Golden-ringed is black and yellow, but it is much longer and the yellow on the abdomen is in the form of bands or rings. Whereas the yellow on the abdomen of the Club-tail is likened to a line of exclamation marks decreasing in size – one below the other. Surprisingly, I have received reports of Golden-ringed from the Wye at Caplar, where club-tails are quite common. It is most definitely not Golden-ringed territory, so I'm sure the observer mis-identified Club-tailed Dragonfly.

Immature and female Black-tailed Skimmers are black and yellow and almost the same size as a Club-tailed, but the pattern of yellow is much more extensive; and don't forget the eyes!

Behaviour

Walking along the river bank from mid to late May recording newly emerged Club-tails is very exciting. It is the beginning of the dragonfly season, they are nationally scarce dragonflies and the extent and range of the Herefordshire population has received very little previous monitoring. However, I am a head teacher, so recording trips at this time of year are limited to weekends. There are only two, or maybe three, weekends during the second half of May. If this brief window of opportunity is further curtailed by the weather, my recording for that year may be very limited.

However, I have had some very successful outings when I have been able to examine bright black and yellow Club-tails sat on nettles or a large dock leaf or maybe a fast expanding plant of Hogweed. I am frequently first alerted to the presence of one when I disturb it as I push through the waist-high tangle of vegetation overhanging the narrow riverside path. My attention is caught by the dragonfly's flight: it can then either, fly some distance, sometimes crossing to the other side of the river, often gaining height and aiming for the tree tops, or, if I am lucky, stay low and drop down into the tall grasses of the neighbouring field. By keeping my eyes fixed upon the spot where it landed I invariably re-find it, approach with caution and am rewarded by excellent views and a photograph opportunity.

It is not unusual to find a Club-tail resting on such an occasion with its wings closed along its abdomen in the manner of a damselfly. It is the only dragonfly I have seen do this *(see photo page 99)*.

I should add at this point that there have been many other outings at the right time of year, when the weather has been perfect, along stretches of river where I have previously recorded Club-tails, when I have drawn a blank. There is an element of luck involved; being in the right place at the right time! I have found that if there are trees dotted along the riverbank, even if the gaps between them allow sunlight to reach the banks, Club-tails are less likely to occur than if there is a stretch of 40 – 50 metres of open bank. Perhaps the presence of trees discourages the emerging larvae from choosing that spot to perform their amazing metamorphosis!

Mature black, green and yellow Club-tails can be found hunting several kilometres from their breeding rivers frequently in orchards or woodland rides or clearings and sometimes along a hedgerow or woodland edge. I have watched two together hawking over a bracken covered hillside on the southern Malverns: presumably they will have originated on the Severn which is seven or eight miles to the east. The record holder for distance from place

A teneral female Club-tail recently emerged from the Wye and still with little colour.

of birth, however, must go to a male that I recorded on the Trelough Lake – the most southerly of the Whitfield Estate Pools in the southwest of Herefordshire (SO4331) on 21st June 1996. This must be at least ten miles of direct dragonfly flight from the Wye.

A female returns alone to the river to oviposit, stroking the water surface with the tip of her abdomen. Such visits are rarely witnessed - I have never seen this happen in Herefordshire!

I cannot finish this section without recounting my most remarkable encounter with a Club-tail. On the 27th of July 1996 I was making a morning reconnaissance of the area around Holme Lacy in preparation for a dragonfly field meeting that I was due to lead in the afternoon. I wanted to see which pools were most likely to provide views of the most species. Just before mid-day I saw a mature male Club-tail sat in a pool of sunlight on some brambles beside a small fishing pool, just under a mile away from the Wye. I was amazed! This was over a month later in the year than I have ever seen one before.

It was nearly time to meet my party, so I placed a net over the rather docile dragonfly, anxious to share my find with others. When we returned to the pool just over an hour later the Club-tail was still there hanging from the side of the net. In the hope of providing all of the party of about twenty with a good view I eased my finger under the insect's legs. He quite readily transferred to my finger where he perched for all to see. Then I persuaded him

off my finger onto the sawn bowl of a felled tree which stood like a table at waist height.

Not only did "my" Club-tail pose in this way for many wonderful photographs, but he then started to perform. He raised his abdomen in the air until it was almost vertical and lowered his head between his legs. Just when I had convinced my party that Clarence the Club-tailed Dragonfly had been patiently coached by me to perform hand-stands and a series of other gymnastic exercises he flew off high into the tree canopy and we never saw him again.

I have searched the literature and as far as I can ascertain this was the latest date a Club-tail has ever been recorded in Britain!

PGG

'My'-aged Club-tail performing his headstand!

The Golden-ringed Dragonfly *Cordulegaster boltonii*

Golden-ringed Dragonfly

PCG

Flight period

The Golden-ringed flies from the beginning of June to early September, but is most likely to be seen from mid-June to mid-August. It can, however, hang on well into the autumn.

Status

National
Widely distributed throughout western England, Scotland and most of Wales. Surprisingly absent from Ireland, considering its westerly distribution in Britain.

Herefordshire – 6/30
One is likely to encounter the Golden-ringed Dragonfly along the western fringes of the county where a sliver of The Black Mountains can be claimed as Herefordshire. Cusop Dingle (SO2440), the Olchon Valley and rills running down from The Black Darren (SO2929) are the only sites where one can be almost certain to find the Golden-ringed.

Golden-ringed Dragonfly
Cordulegaster boltonii

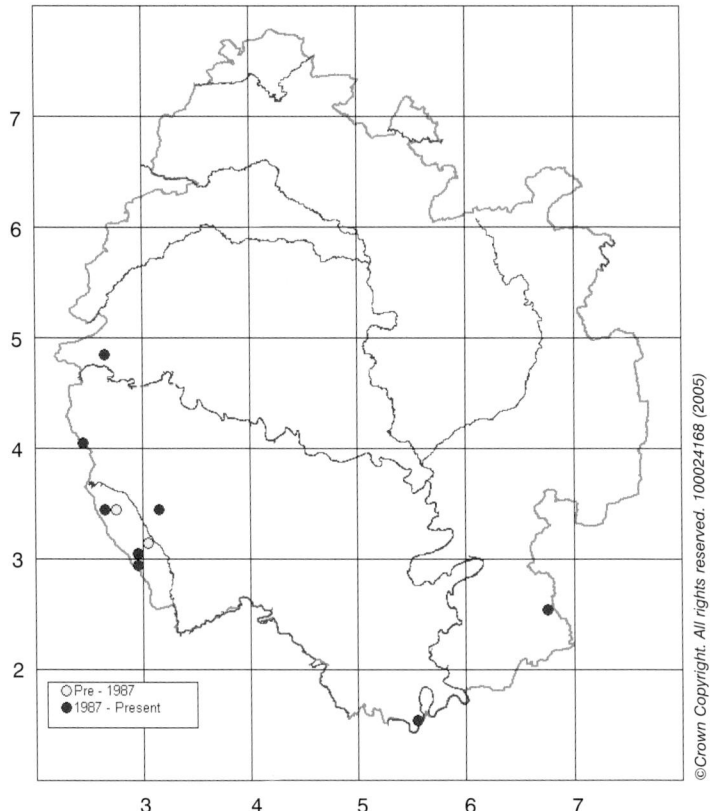

I have received a couple of reliable records from the south east of Herefordshire and I assume these are stragglers from well established breeding colonies in the nearby Forest of Dean. The majority of Gloucestershire records come from three 10km squares – SO50, 60 and 61. The two Herefordshire records are from SO50 and 62. It is always possible that a small breeding population could be discovered on the Wye at Symonds Yat or the Doward following an extension of the colonies in the Forest of Dean.

Habitat

The Golded-ringed breeds in small, often acidic, streams, rivulets or runnels in bogs, or even suitable rivers: often swift flowing in winter, but where the flow is reduced to a trickle in the summer. It is never found in standing water. I have watched them patrolling narrow runnels in Cotton-grass bogs under the Black Darren, but nearby it is equally at home along the exposed sunny stretches of the upper Olchon Brook as it tumbles between rocks and boulders – a truly moorland habitat. In Cusop and Brilley Dingles the breeding stream is deeply cut, and partially shaded by bankside trees. In all cases this species requires a bed of silt, gravel or peaty debris into which the female, with her long, pointed ovipositor, can lay her eggs without fear of them being washed away. In the type of habitat where the Golden-ringed occurs in Herefordshire it is often the only Dragonfly species present.

Description

This is a large dragonfly, almost as long as The Emperor and as long or longer than most of the hawkers. It is black with striking golden rings encircling each segment of the abdomen: it is unlikely to be confused with any other species. Both sexes are similar, but the male which is smaller is slightly waisted and club-shaped. The female appears even longer than she is because of her unique, protruding, pointed black ovipositor.

Behaviour

The Golden-ringed is a stunning looking insect that one is unlikely to overlook. It flies low, close to the water surface following the twists and turns of the stream along a considerable length of beat. It frequently stalls and veers to the bank-side where it peers at some minute detail which has caught its attention. If one sits beside such a stream or rivulet one can watch it pass and re-pass; from time to time it will return to a favourite perch and hang in the perpendicular manner of other long-bodied dragonflies. On the sunny upper reaches of the Olchon Brook I have seen them sunning themselves on large mid-stream boulders.

The Downy Emerald *Cordulia aenea*

Flight Period

Nationally, Downy Emeralds are most frequently recorded form late May unitl late July
I have recorded them in Herefordshire on the following dates:- 25.6.95 (5), 1.8.95 (2), 15.8.96
(3), 16.7.00 (1), 26.7.02 (1).

Status

National

Scarce away from its stronghold in Surrey and Hampshire the Downy Emerald has a very
scattered distribution. It occurs in isolated sites, stretching from Devon to the Highlands of
Scotland with gaps of a hundred miles, or so, between some colonies. There are just two or
three sites in south west Ireland.

Herefordshire – 1/30

The county's only breeding[1] site for the Downy Emerald is of national significance because
it links the Gloucestershire sites in the Forest of Dean to the Shropshire sites which are
clustered around Shrewsbury. The link, however, is not an active one in so far as individuals
from these isolated colonies are unlikely to inter-relate. They are considered to be relict
populations from an earlier period[2], and consequently must be very vulnerable.

The numbers of individuals I have recorded on each visit are very small, which would
make one wonder how the colony might persist. However, this Herefordshire site is on a
private estate and access has been difficult. The only visit when I saw more than two or
three was my discovery visit in late June 1995 when I saw five. All my other visits have been
in July and August – very much at the late end of the flight period (15th August 1996 was
the latest recorded British sighting for 1996). It is very likely that if I had been able to visit
this pool in late May or early June I might have recorded many more individuals.

"The Downy Emerald Pool" will be described in greater detail under the "habitat"
section, but it is relevant at this point to mention that within a hundred metres and within
the same wood, there is another much larger pool which appears to meet all the habitat
requirements for the Downy Emerald. However, I have never observed it on this larger
pool, but if I had visited the wood in late May or early June I might have recorded it here as
well.

The proximity of this larger pool raises another fascinating conundrum. Herefordshire's
greatest Victorian entomologist lived in Tarrington, close to my "Downy Emerald Wood".
John Henry Wood (1841 – 1914) was primarily a lepidopterist and a dipterist – both his
collection of microlepidoptera (tiny moths) and diptera (flies) are in the British Museum.

However, he recorded many other groups of insects including Dragonflies. His list of
Dragonflies[3] names the large pool next to the Downy Emerald pool as a site for several
species including Four-spotted Chaser, Common Darter and Ruddy Darter. The latter was

---

1 By the strictest definition of "Breeding" we cannot claim absolute proof of breeding for Downy Emerald. I have
  observed them "incop" and ovipositing, but no exuviae have been found and no freshly emerged tenerals have
  been recorded.
2 Merritt R. et al. 1996
3 Woolhope Naturalists Field Club, 1954.

Downy Emerald Dragonfly
Cordulia aenea

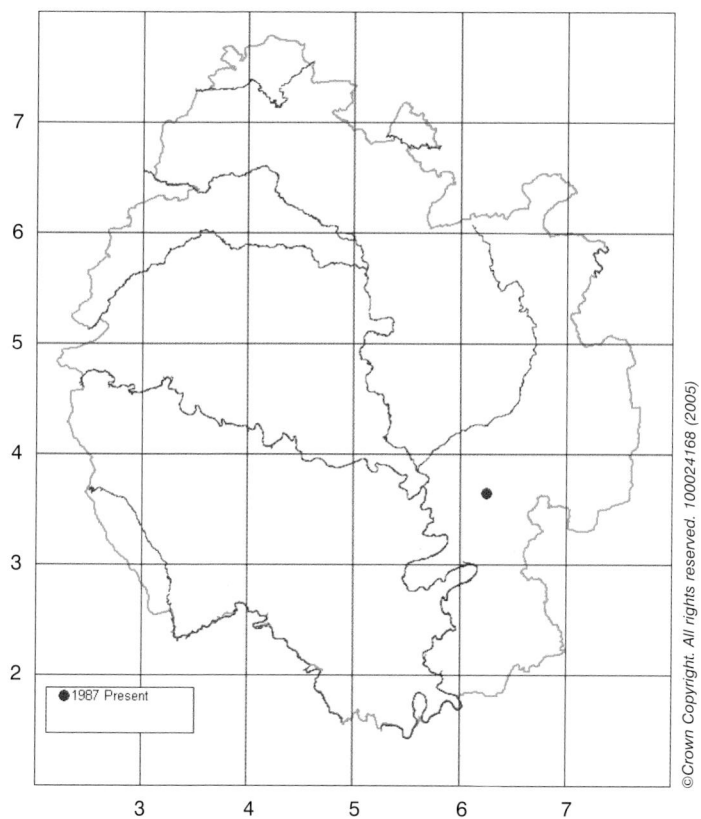

rare in Britain, especially in the West Midlands at the turn of the last century, and such a record would be treated with scepticism if it had not originated from a naturalist of such high esteem.

I make this point because I believe that if John Wood knew these pools in the late 19th century/early 20th century, and if he was alert enough to separate the Ruddy Darter from the Common Darter, it is unlikely that he would have failed to record Downy Emerald. If it was not, it questions the theory that the current fragmented distribution of isolated British colonies are relicts of a bygone age.

Further evidence which should add credence to the theory that our Herefordshire Downy Emeralds are recent additions to "the county list" is of a more contemporary nature. Parker[4] visited this pool in 1977 and recorded Red-eyed Damselfly but made no mention of Downy Emerald, and ten years later on the 12th July 1987 I made my first visit to the pool and yet despite an impressive list, I did not record Downy Emerald. Perhaps dispersal is

---

4   Parker D.M. (1978)

more common than we suppose and our Herefordshire Downy Emeralds are more recent colonists. I hope this is the case because we have at least one other pool in south east Herefordshire – in fact, even nearer to the Forest of Dean colonies – than our current site – which looks to be perfect Downy Emerald habitat, and even hosts a thriving colony of Red-eyed Damselflies which appear to be favoured associates of the Downy Emerald.

Habitat

Our one site is a woodland pool with over-hanging broad-leaved trees, about the size of four tennis courts. Much has been written about Downy Emerald habitat, and our Herefordshire site is typical. I shall describe this one site in greater detail, but would urge readers not to make too much of information gleaned from just one site.

Alder and Oak lean over the eastern and southern margins of the pool. The western and northern sides are more open with Rose, Dogwood and Willow shrubs providing a 15-20 metre buffer of lower canopy between the pool and the main Oak wood. *Typha* grows among these shrubs and borders the pond, where it grows with Water Horse-tail *Equisetum fluviatile*. There are a few small patches of Yellow Water-lily *Nuphar lutea* extending into the pool from the eastern margins which, along with rafts of blanket algae, form the required basking perches for the Red-eyed Damselflies.

The "Downy Emerald" Pool.

There is plenty of submerged aquatic vegetation in the pond. Rigid Hornwort *Ceratophyllum demersum* chokes the open more sunny sides of the pond, and in the shaded edges where the leaf litter is considerable, there are accumulations of the aquatic moss *Amblystegium riparium*. The two duckweeds – *Lemna minor* and *Lemna trisulca* occupy much of the water surface in the sunnier parts of the pool.

The neighbouring pool (the size of a football pitch and slightly more) is bounded on all sides by the predominately Oak woodland. A swathe of Bulrush *Typha sp.* four or five metres thick surrounds the lake on the north and eastern shores. There are carpets of Yellow and White Water-lilies across a third of the lake's surface; the other two thirds are open water. This abuts the shaded southern borders, where the lake-side trees deposit ample leaf-litter for any so desiring Downy Emerald larva.

Description

The Downy Emerald is a medium sized dragonfly with a generally dark appearance. Before I continue I must now remind my readers that all of those that I have seen have been in the later half of their flight period – my one June sighting was towards the end of that month.

As my visits have been late in the season I presume I have only seen mature or aging Downy Emeralds. They have not appeared to be very green, but rather a uniformly dark colour. I have not been able to see one at rest, but their flight has been steady enough on occasions for me to focus on one with my binoculars. Then I am able to note the green eyes, head and thorax and the glinting metallic sheen – I couldn't see that it was very downy, but I have observed this feature subsequently. It was "waisted" and the narrow segments of the abdomen towards the thorax were a lighter colour. Below the restriction towards the end of the abdomen it was very dark and of no dicernable colour until a closer view was afforded. I could then see that most of the abdomen and especially the bulbous lower half was a metallic bronze, almost maroon colour. This caught me by surprise, I had been expecting a much greener dragonfly. The downy hairs on the thorax are a ginger/buff colour and merge into the similarly yellow bases of both pairs of wings.

The female's abdomen is broader than the males and so she presents as a chunkier dragonfly, but similarly coloured.

Behaviour

I had been scanning the pool with binoculars trying to count Red-eyed Damselflies. My attention was taken by an Emperor flying a metre or so above the water surface in the middle of the pool, and then I was aware of a smaller dragonfly below it. I followed it flying very close to the surface, hovering, then flashing forward a short distance, then cruising, hovering and dashing again. Often it clashed with another of the same species and they whirled and chased flying up as they broke away. It then clashed with a similarly sized dragonfly which I could see was a Four-spotted Chaser.

Soon after I had started to follow it in the binoculars I knew this was my first Downy Emerald, mainly because it was so noticeably 'waisted', but as I continue to watch I could see its bright metallic green head and eyes and the bronzy-green thorax.

There was a minimum of three and sometimes four, mostly keeping close to the edges of the pool, which meant I got regular close views.

I returned to the pool on the 1st August 1995. When I arrived I immediately recognised the rapid, low and rather manic flight of the Downy Emerald and I also noticed how the tip of its abdomen seemed to droop down, maybe because it is 'waisted' this is an optical illusion, but it helps to identify this dragonfly from a distance. Its flying posture is in this way, similar to that of the Emperor. I also noticed how often it stopped and hovered, often turning to face the shore.

I had only been watching it for about ten minutes when it veered violently to one side and appeared to attack a second one that I had not previously noticed. In fact it was not an attack, it had grabbed a female and they flew up, in tandem, to the tree canopy. Later in the afternoon I watched a female ovipositing; whether or not it was the same female I can't say. She was flying low across the pond surface tapping the tail of her abdomen into the water in the way I have often seen Common Darters when they oviposit in tandem. However, the she continued for ten to fifteen minutes entirely alone. Not only was the male not joined to her, but he was not in attendance, not even at the pool!

The larva takes from two to four years to mature. It has long antennae and fine bristling hairs on it's legs, because it must hunt by touch. It lives in the un-decomposed leaf litter at the edges of pools, probably clinging upside down to the underside of a leaf during the day and hunting by night.

It is likely that if I am able to revisit this pool earlier in the year – end of May or early June – I will find a higher density of Downy Emeralds and they will appear greener!

Addendum

The wood in which the "Downy Emerald Pool" and its neighbouring lake are situated has changed ownership and the new owners are conservation minded and very obliging. Unfortunately, the exciting new freedom to visit the pool has not resulted in any Downy Emerald records for 2005. Steve Roe searched diligently for exuvia at the pool on a weekly basis from mid-May through to July, and I accompanied him on several occasions. Hours of searching and patiently watching both pools revealed no sign of the Downy Emerald. I have one theory which casts the Emperor in the role of villain. In June and early July on each of our visits there were four or five Emperors patrolling territories around the edges of the pool. There were no other dragonfly species on the pool – a few Ruddy Darters were in the marginal vegetation in July, and Broad-bodied Chasers and Southern Hawkers sometimes could be seen in the adjacent woodland rides, but the Emperors retained exclusive rights to the water surface of the pool.

Have the Emperors driven off the Downy Emeralds?

During our visits in earlier years I only once had an Emperor on this pool and that was a singleton.

Over the last thirty years there has been a dramatic expansion of the Emperor's range *(see Emperor – status)*. An interesting area for research would be the effect of the spread of this aggressive dragonfly on other species.

We will continue to monitor the site and hope that the Downy Emerald is not now lost to Herefordshire!

The Chasers and Skimmers

These are medium sized robust dragonflies that fly low across the water surface. They are mostly blue or yellow with distinguishing dark or black markings. With their proportionately shorter abdomens they perch horizontally rather than hang in the way of the longer bodied hawkers.

There are three British species of chasers and two occur in Herefordshire – the Broad-bodied and Four-spotted. The third – the Scarce Chaser has recently extended its range into Worcestershire on the River Avon. I saw one there in 1998 and then in 2004 the population seemed to explode and they were reported as, "very well established". We must stay alert for this rare riverine species on the Wye.

Of the two British skimmers, Herefordshire can boast just the Black-tailed. The Keeled Skimmer is a dragonfly of acid bogs and flushes – a type of habitat almost non-existent in Herefordshire.

LC

Black-tailed Skimmer basking on stones in the dried up riverbed of the River Wye, Holme Lacy.

The Four-spotted Chaser *Libellula quadrimaculata*

The Four-spotted Chaser.

Flight Period
Most likely to be seen in June and July. It normally emerges about the same time as the Broad-bodied Chaser.

Status

National
Widespread throughout Britain and Ireland – reaching as far north as the Orkneys. However, the Four-spotted Chaser is not uniformly distributed across its range. In some areas it is extremely common, but in others it can be hard to find and it is completely absent from some sites that would appear ideal.

Herefordshire – 10/30
It is widespread but very local. With little more than a dozen sites scattered across the county it is always exciting to come across one in Herefordshire.

    I have no absolute proof of breeding, but I have recorded them at the same two sites annually for a considerable number of years, and I have observed them ovipositing: the

Four-spotted Chaser
Libellula quadrimaculata

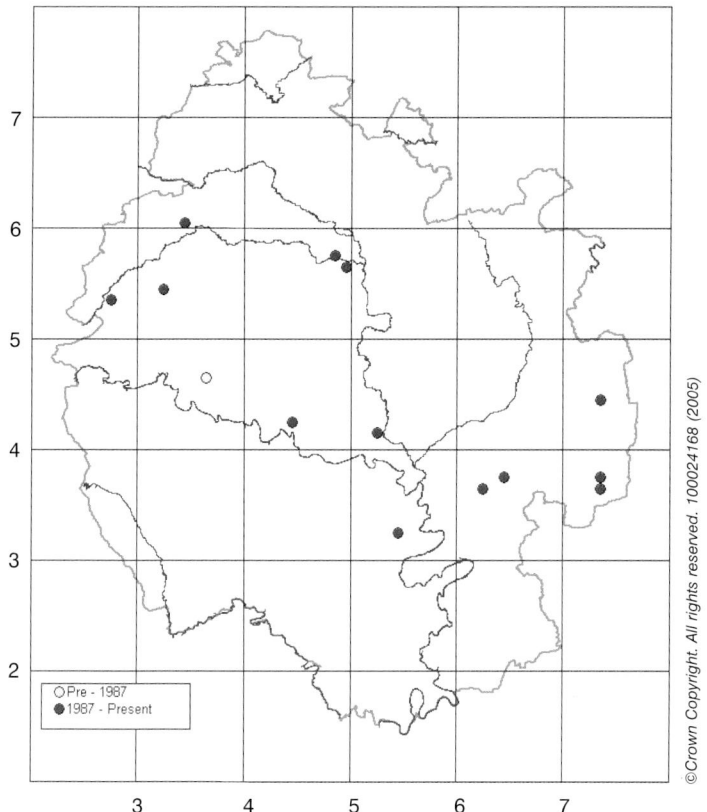

evidence is circumstantial but compelling! On 27th June 1993 I counted 30 Four-spotted Chasers on a pool not much larger than a tennis court at the dis-used Mathon Gravel Pit; there had been 20 there the week before.

Habitat

In Britain the Four-spotted Chaser is most common on acidic bogs in moorland and upland areas. Less frequently it can be found on ponds, lakes and canals and is an occasional rare visitor to garden ponds.

It is a migratory species with major influxes arriving from continental Europe in favoured years. It is also a great wanderer which means it could turn up anywhere and the presence of one or even two or three Four-spotted Chasers at a pond does not indicate breeding.

Description

Unlike the other two species of chaser in Britain the male and female Four-spotted Chaser are almost identical. They are most likely to be confused with a dull mature female Broad-bodied Chaser, but they are noticeably slimmer with a more pointed dark tail to the abdomen. Their head and eyes are dark brown and the thorax and upper part of the abdomen is a light gingery brown.

While watching Four-spotted Chasers at Stretton Sugwas Gravel Pit I was confused by some partially blue maturing Black-tailed Skimmers. All Black-tailed Skimmers start yellow and then the males mature to become mostly blue. These were part dull yellow and part blue and when they were flying too far away to see if there were spots on the wings they caused me some difficulty.

However, when one is treated to a view of the Four-spotted Chaser motionless on a prominent pool-side perch one is left in no doubt about the identification of this dragonfly because it has a very distinctive and unique wing pattern, which also accounts for its name. Not only does it have a conspicuous dark pterostigma but it has a second dark spot or blotch in the middle of the costa (the front or leading edge of the wing). There is a narrow golden line leading from the middle spot close to the costa, down to the base of the wing. There are dark brown patches at the bases of the wings which are especially marked on the hind wings. This pattern of two dark brown spots is repeated on all four wings, which rather flippantly suggests to me that it should be re-named the Eight-spotted Chaser!

While watching a pair mating then ovipositing at Stretton Sugwas on 6th June 2004 I observed that the female was noticeably larger than the male and brighter. I can find no references to such a distinction and I have not observed it previously so I must assume that this was just the general variation which can exist between individuals and bears no relevance to a difference between the sexes.

Behaviour

Males are aggressively territorial. They take up perches on pond-side vegetation from which they chase off intruders, or launch themselves to intercept a female. They are often found at the same ponds as Broad-bodied Chasers and I have watched these larger 'cousins' driving off Four-spotted Chasers, but I have also recorded the reverse.

In June 1993 there were exceptional numbers of Four-spotted Chasers at one well established sheltered sunny pool at Mathon Gravel Pit. On the 20th I estimated that there were about 25 chasing and buzzing each other around the edges of the pool with little chance that any one dragonfly could possibly defend a territory. With several 'punch-ups' occurring at any one time the dry, brittle, rustling sound of their wings was audible before the pond came into sight. A lone Emperor cruised the pond, above the chasers and mostly in the middle, but for most of the time untroubled by their frenzied activity. Broad-bodied Chasers that I had seen at this pool earlier in the month were nowhere to be seen. A week later there were even more Four-spotted Chasers on this pool and I watched one aggressively see off a much larger female Broad-bodied Chaser. I wonder if a preponderance of Four-spotted Chasers will prevail even against the larger Broad-bodied Chaser and allow them supremacy of the 'near surface habitat niche'?

Mating takes place in flight and is very brief. On 6th June 2004 at Stretton Sugwas I watched a male grab an ovipositing female. They joined in the 'wheel position' and flew in this position along the margin of the pool before breaking apart, after which the female resumed the tapping of the tip of her abdomen onto the water surface. The male had got past her previous mate and re-fertilised her with his sperm. He then flew in attendance to stave off similar assaults from other rapacious suitors.

Although they do spend long periods of time perched, Four-spotted Chasers seem to spend more time patrolling than Broad-bodied Chasers. They fly low and fast in a darting way, frequently pausing to hover. While hovering they allow confirmation of identification because the four (or eight in total) wing spots are clearly visible.

During the twenty years I have been surveying Herefordshire's dragonflies I have recorded Four-spotted Chasers regularly at the two favoured sites I have mentioned, but only in 1993 have they occurred in almost 'plague' proportions.

The Old Pool at Stretton Sugwas Gravel Pit where I have watched the Four-spotted Chaser ovipositing.

The Broad-bodied Chaser *Libellula depressa*

Broad-bodied Chaser – male

Flight Period

On the wing from the beginning of May to the end of July.
This is an early season species, most abundant from mid-May until late July. August records are rare.

Status

National
Widespread and common in southern England, south Wales and the Midlands, becoming less common northwards up to a line running across the country from the Dee to the Humber. Absent from northern England, Scotland and Ireland.

Herefordshire – 28/30
The Broad-bodied Chaser can turn up almost anywhere! They are rarely seen in more than two's or three's and can be over-looked at a pool because they spend long periods perching on pond-side vegetation, but at other times can be very active.

They breed in a wide variety of still water bodies including many garden and farm ponds which, because of their widespread, unmapped and private nature have been poorly recorded. There can be no doubt that there should be many more dots on the distribution map for this species.

Broad-bodied Chaser
Libellula depressa

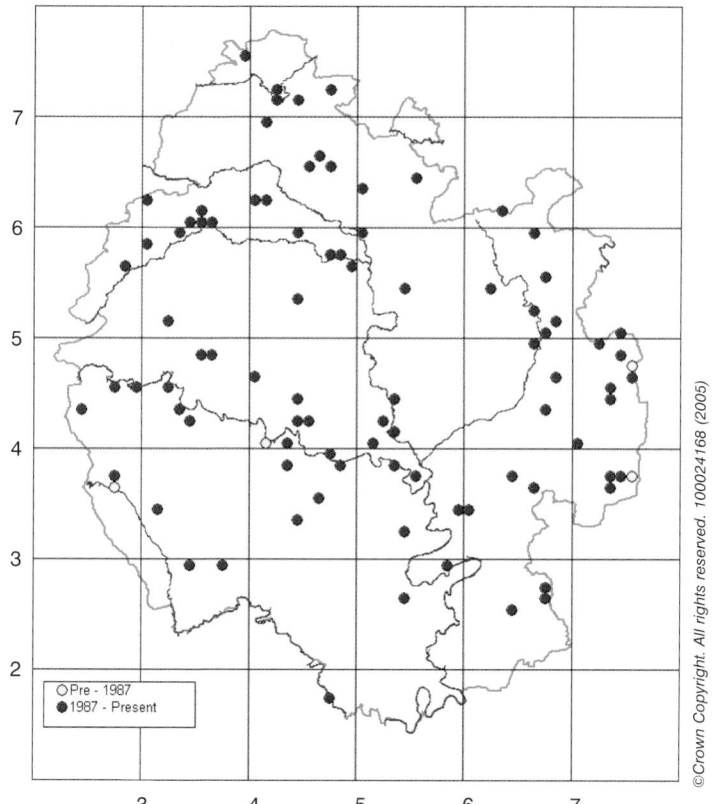

Legend:
- ○ Pre - 1987
- ● 1987 - Present

Habitat

Most sunny sites with standing water are suitable for Broad-bodied Chasers and they will even breed in mildly polluted ponds such as the one just west of Bircher beside the B4362 (SO4765).

They are just as likely to be found on some of our larger lakes as in a bath-sized garden pond, and it appears to make no difference whether it is a well vegetated long established pool or bare open water recently created – maybe at a gravel pit. At Stretton Sugwas Gravel Pit I have watched females ovipositing in the main lake, which is the size of two football pitches with just a few scattered patches of submerged colonizing plants such as Stoneworts *Chara sp.* and thread-leaved pondweeds *Potamogeton sp.* and no marginal vegetation. At the same gravel pit there is an old spring-fed pond in one corner with a rich diversity of submerged, floating and emergent vegetation and I have seen Broad-bodied Chasers ovipositing here as well. However, if they are at lakes and large pools they will most likely be found around the shore line.

I have heard stories from other parts of the country of ponds being dug one year and Broad-bodied Chasers emerging from the same pond the following year. We can almost match that in Herefordshire. Peter Tierney is a consultant in farmland conservation who has a farm near Longtown close to the Black Mountains. In 2000 he dug a new pool on a windswept hillside, and in 2002, he had Broad-bodied Chasers emerging.

Description

In rugby parlance, this is the prop-forward of the dragonfly world. The Irish seem to name their dragonflies more appropriately than we do, and if the Broad-bodied Chaser was more than just an isolated historical record for them, I could imagine they would call it the 'Chunky Chaser'.

When they are mature, males and females are coloured very differently. The broad, flattened abdomen of the male is predominantly gun-metal blue, with lemon yellow lateral spots along the edges of the middle segments. He has a dark brown head and thorax and sizeable dark brown patches at the wing bases. He also has pale antehumeral stripes.

The female (and immature male) has similar patterning and colour on her head, thorax and wings to that of the male, but her abdomen which is even broader than the male's, is a striking combination of brown and yellow reminiscent of a Hornet, for which it is not uncommonly mistaken.

With age, females darken and the bright yellow fades, then as she becomes a really 'elderly lady' parts of her abdomen assume the blue colouring of the male, while the tail, with patches and streaks elsewhere, appears to be almost black.

PGG

Female Broad-bodied Chaser.

I have only been confused by such individuals on two occasions both of which were in August. One was 31st August 1997 at Mathon Gravel Pit.

Behaviour

Males are aggressively territorial, but rather than patrolling their territory, they sit out on waterside vegetation from where they will launch an attack on other dragonflies that might invade 'their' pool or 'their' stretch of bank.

As a frequent visitor to garden ponds they are the best known of the early summer dragonflies . They indulge in long periods of perching and basking in the sunshine so it is easier to get a really good view of them. When they leave a perch to chase off an intruder, or to hunt they frequently return to the same spot, which further facilitates viewing and photography. Normally they will choose a dead twig or dead rush stalk as a perch with their body tilted towards the sun. Their distinctive shape, bright colours and availability for recognition by the uninitiated, regularly recruits new members for the ever-growing 'dragonfly fan-club'.

Females are more frequently encountered away from water which probably makes it more likely that the general public will not realise they are dragonflies and wrongly associate them with wasps or Hornets. When they do return to the pond to breed, mating is a brief engagement and then the female, almost straight afterwards, oviposits unattached by slapping the tip of her abdomen into the water surface to wash free the eggs. The male often hovers nearby to ward off competitors.

On three or four occasions I have arrived at pools where the number of male Broad-bodied Chasers dashing across the surface of the pond has been between six and ten. The pools have all been open, shallow, relatively small ponds with no tall emergent vegetation or nearby trees or bushes[1]. There has been no apparent pattern to their uncharacteristically incessant frenzied flight. There have been clashes and brief aerial combat, but for the majority of the time they have continued uninterrupted in the weaving of their zig-zag patterns. I have watched them flying in this manner during the middle of the day for over an hour. I could not say if it is the same individuals or whether they are 'substituted' from time to time. At the Burcott Pool their numbers were more than doubled by Black-tailed Skimmers. It is more usual for Black-tailed Skimmers to fly 'on patrol' for quite long periods.

When two Four-spotted Chasers were added to the mix at Denby Hall Pool, it was very difficult to separate the three species and count how many there were of each, but in total, there were more than a dozen all flying purposefully, close to the surface, mostly in straight lines but in a random variation of directions.

In a wide cross-section of literature I have been unable to find any accounts of this type of behaviour. The only explanation I can offer is that in the absence of suitable prominent perches, when confronted by several rival males the Broad-bodied Chasers have been obliged to stay on the wing in order to guard territories that have not been definable to the human eye.

---

1   Burcott Pool (on northern edge of Hereford) (SO5242) – 24/7/96. Toll House Mill-pool, nr Kington (SO2856) – 20/7/97. Denby Hall Pool (SO3460) – 20/6/98. The Buzzards Pool (SO4162) – 24/6/01.

Black-tailed Skimmer *Orthetrum cancellatum*

Black-tailed Skimmer – male.

Flight Period
Its long flight period extends from late May to early September but it is most abundant from the second week in June until Mid-August.

Status

National
The Black-tailed Skimmer increased its range considerably in the second half of the last century. It is now widespread across southern England with a foot-hold in south Wales. It is largely concentrated south of a line from The Wash to Bristol, but is continuing to colonise areas to the north, extending almost to Scotland. It has a patchy distribution in central and western Ireland.

Herefordshire – 23/30
During his survey in 1977 Parker[1] failed to record this species in Herefordshire. However, when considering its history in neighbouring counties, even though it was not mentioned by Peers[2] when he wrote about Radnorshire Dragonflies in 1985, it would seem likely it was overlooked by Parker! There are a few early records from Gloucestershire[3] from the early 30's and 40's and then it quickly became established and widespread in the second half of the century. There are no pre-war records for Worcestershire[4], but plenty from the 50's and 60's onwards.

I counted at least six males and a female ovipositing at Mathon Gravel Pit on the 27th June 1986 and that was the first recorded sighting for Herefordshire, but I expect they had

1   Parker D.M. (1978)
2   Peers M. (1985)
3   Holland S. (1991)
4   Averill M. (1996)

Black-tailed Skimmer
Orthetrum cancellatum

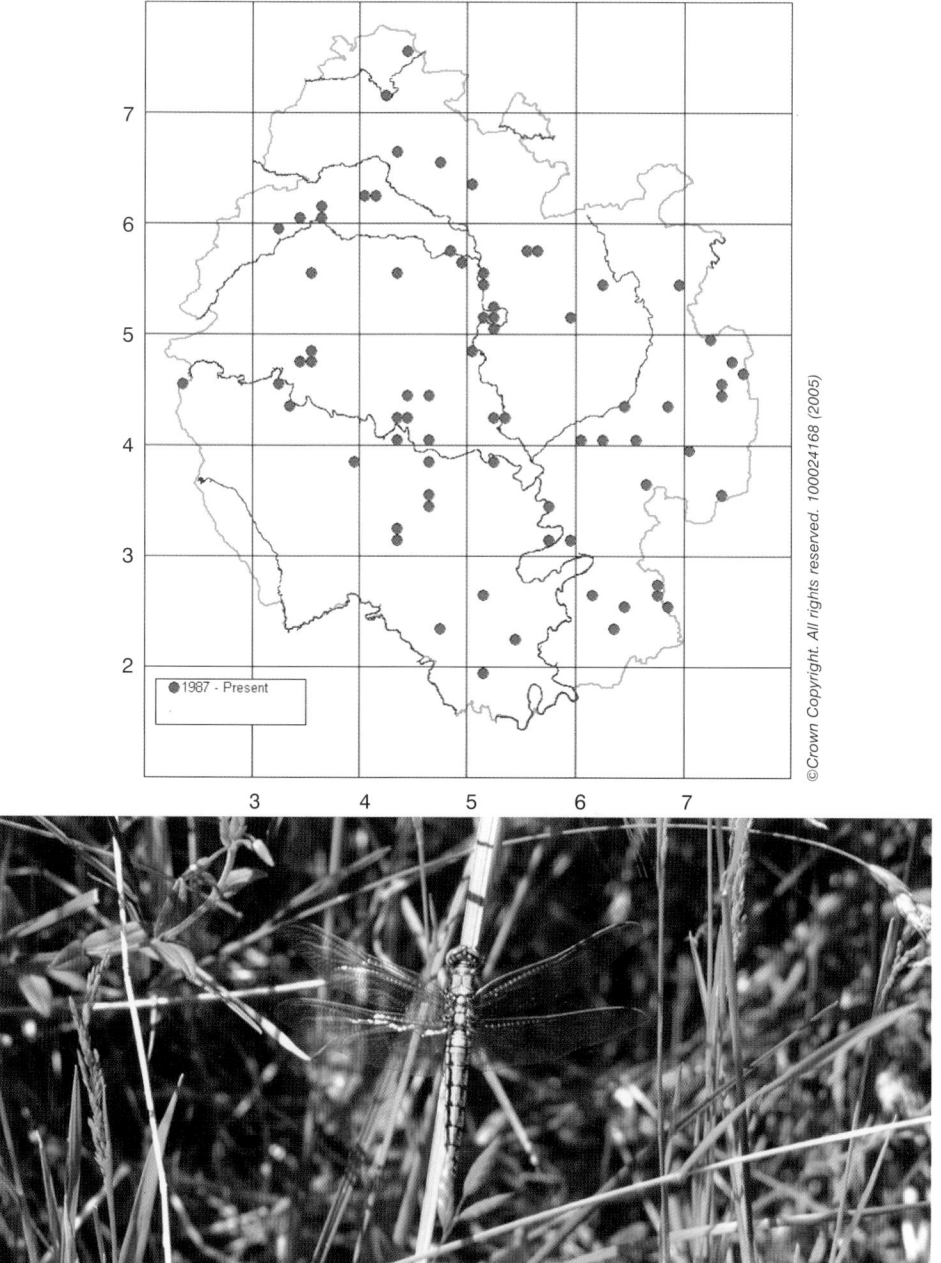

1987 - Present

Black-tailed Skimmer – juvenile.

PGG

123

been there since extraction started over twenty years earlier. It was perfect habitat and with several well established colonies only a few miles away in Worcestershire, it would be surprising if the Mathon population were as recent immigrants to Herefordshire as I was. At the time, Bodenham was a well established gravel pit providing ideal habitat; even though it was further west and north, I expect Black-tailed Skimmers were there as well.

They are now well established across the County. The Leech Pool at Clifford (SO2345) is as far west as you can go in Herefordshire, and I have twice counted up to half a dozen males there skimming close to the wet muddy shores (16th August 1997 and 7th August 2002). A new pool at The Brakes just west of Ludlow (SO4475) had Black-tailed Skimmers patrolling territories all the way round its shores and this is very close to the northern most Herefordshire county boundary (17th July 1999).

At Stretton Sugwas Gravel Pit where gravel extraction has now ceased there remains a mosaic of shallow "naked" pools – a Black-tailed Skimmer's paradise and not surprisingly they can be found there in remarkable concentrations. On the 8th August 2003 I estimated there were between 50 and 100 males. Similar numbers were there on the 24th July 1998 and the 25th July 1996. There were in excess of 50 at Docklow Fishing Pools (SO5557) on the 21st July 1997 and at Mathon Gravel Pit on the 27th June 1993.

I haven't recorded any in the extreme southwest of the county, but this is most likely because of a lack of suitable habitat.

N.B see under 'Habitat' the note for Werndee Pool which is evidence that the Black-tailed Skimmer is keen to exploit any means of further extending its range to the west.

Habitat

It is especially attracted to pools bordered, at least in places, by stretches of bare ground on which it settles in a prone position maximising the warmth of the sun. It is an early coloniser of new pools because it is well suited to the bare muddy banks. The proliferation of gravel pits after the war associated with the expansion of the construction industry, and the building of the motorway network, undoubtedly accelerated the spread of this species northwards and westwards across southern England.

It is now so common that it even appears on pools with lush marginal vegetation, so long as there are some bare poolside sun-bathing areas. Many fishing pools have a Black-tailed Skimmer on every jetty or trodden down fisherman's pitch. On the 25th July 1998 at Werndee Pool (SO4723) there were no bare banks, or fishermen's platforms, but beside the pool there were mounds of algal bloom, which had been raked out and left to bake in the sun. There were seven such mounds and all but one had a basking male Black-tailed Skimmer. Also towards the southwest at Weston Farm Pool (SO3245) there were at least twelve males criss-crossing the surface of the pool. It is the most unlikely habitat: there is no shore or muddy bank and the pool is surrounded by tall emergent vegetation. There is a drain coming into the pool from the farm across the road and this probably causing the rafts of algae that maybe act as a substitute "shore".

In high summer when the flow of the Wye recedes, extensive shingle beaches develop and Black-tailed Skimmers enjoy the warmth of these exposed stoney surfaces (*see photo on page 112*). On the 27th July 1996 there were over twenty Black-tailed Skimmers beside the Wye near Holme Lacy Church (SO5734). They were criss-crossing shallow lagoons that had been created by the falling river levels, and I noted several females ovipositing. I assume winter floodwaters would flush away these eggs or any resulting lavae. I also observed Black-tailed Skimmers on shingle 'beaches' beside the River Teme at Criftin Ford (SO4271) on the 4th August 2003.

Description

This is a neat, compact, medium sized dragonfly, slim in comparison to the similarly coloured Broad-bodied Chaser. The mature male has a gun-metal blue abdomen with relatively inconspicuous dull yellow edges to the central segments (S3-S8). The last three segments of the abdomen are black – hence the "black tail". The head and thorax can vary from greenish-grey to brown and in very bright specimens the downy thorax is a rusty gold colour. The legs are black and apart from a narrow black pterostigma the wings are clear. This is a helpful feature when distinguishing Black-tailed Skimmer from Broad-bodied Chaser which has a large dark-brown patch at the base of each wing.

Females and immature males, are coloured completely differently: they are all yellow (the thorax of the female is more brown than yellow) with two lines of black curves running down eitherside of the abdomen.

Complications arise in old-age: elderly males lose the yellow edges to the abdomen and as the females mature the yellow dulls to grey and even a blue/grey similar to an aging male, but of course they don't have the black tail. This caused me to have a surge of excitement and then confusion on one occasion, because the very similar Keeled Skimmer has no black tail, and has never been recorded in Herefordshire.

Behaviour

"Skimmer" by name, 'skimmer' by nature: Black-tailed Skimmers fly close to the surface, patrolling a stretch of shore-line. They will fly back and forth along their beat and then rest up at a favoured perch. This is normally, flat unvegetated mud or gravel where they might chose a favoured stone; sometimes it will be a dead branch or the decking of a fisherman's jetty. Every so often they will flash out away from the margins and criss-cross the pond flying rapid purposeful tangents.

It is rare to see a female at the pond and if one does it is invariably because she has returned to the pond to oviposit. She does this by dipping the tip of her abdomen into the water, normally with the male in attendance.

When I first started to take an interest in dragonflies I was perplexed to discover a pond with over twenty females at rest on surrounding vegetation, and no males in sight. It took a little while for the penny to drop: the "females" were all newly emerged immature males and females, which at this stage are all yellow with black markings and indistinguishable from each other.

Many years later (30.5.98), I was watching a mass emergence of Black-tailed Skimmers from the deserted Arrow Fisheries lagoons just south of Leominster (SO4956). During a twenty minute period between 30 and 50 teneral Black-tails launched themselves skywards on 'wet-look' glistening wings with a rather laboured fluttering flight. As I watched them disappearing from sight I became aware of an "over-sized Swift" – a Hobby, sweeping above me, adjusting its arc to coincide with a dispersing, freshly emerged Black-tailed Skimmer. Through my binoculars I watched the Hobby catch the young dragonflies in its talons and then transfer them to its beak, in the way I might transfer raspberries from the cane to my mouth!

In September I have watched post breeding, family parties of Hobbies feeding on Craneflies in this way in Worcestershire, and I have seen Hobbies swooping to catch dragonflies over pools on the Lizard in Cornwall, but this is the only occasion when I have observed this remarkably dextrous raptor feeding on dragonflies in Herefordshire.

The Darters

Darters are small dragonflies appearing mostly in the second half of 'the season' with some 'hanging on' well into November. Generally males are reddish and females yellowish. The Common and Ruddy Darters are widespread and frequently encountered. By way of an exception the male Black Darter is black rather than red but I have only ever found it on one pool in the north of the County. The other darter which has been recorded in Herefordshire is the Red-Veined Darter, which is a very rarely seen migrant.

Although the two common red darters can first be found on the wing in early July their appearance at many ponds is not synchronised. On numerous occasions I have visited pools in Herefordshire where I know both species are plentiful. I have found only Ruddy Darters throughout July; Common Darters start to show up at the pools in early August and by mid August they outnumber the Ruddy Darters. At the end of August Ruddy Darters are very scarce and by mid September they have all finished flying. Common Darters will continue to emerge even into the first week of October.

Do the Ruddy Darters drive the larger Common Darters away from the pools? This would seem unlikely because Ruddy Darters are generally less territorial than their larger relative. I can only assume that the Ruddy Darter has a more particular preference to stay close to water whereas the Common Darter prefers to hunt further afield and returns to the pool later in the season to breed.

Common Darter – male.

The **Common Darter** *Sympetrum striolatum*

Common Darter – male.

Flight Period

Common Darters emerge in late June and fly until early November. They are most abundant in August, September and October.

In recent years this hardy little dragonfly has more regularly extended its flight period into November as our winter climate becomes less severe. They were normally killed off by October frosts, but in the last few years they have been collapsing due to old age – floundering on the surface of the pond with battered or missing wings, too feeble to remain airborne.

Status

National
Common throughout England, Wales and Ireland giving way to its very close relative the Highland Darter towards the north of Scotland.

Herefordshire – 29/30
Common and widespread throughout the County with very large numbers occurring at some sites in mid to late summer.

Common Darter
Sympetrum striolatum

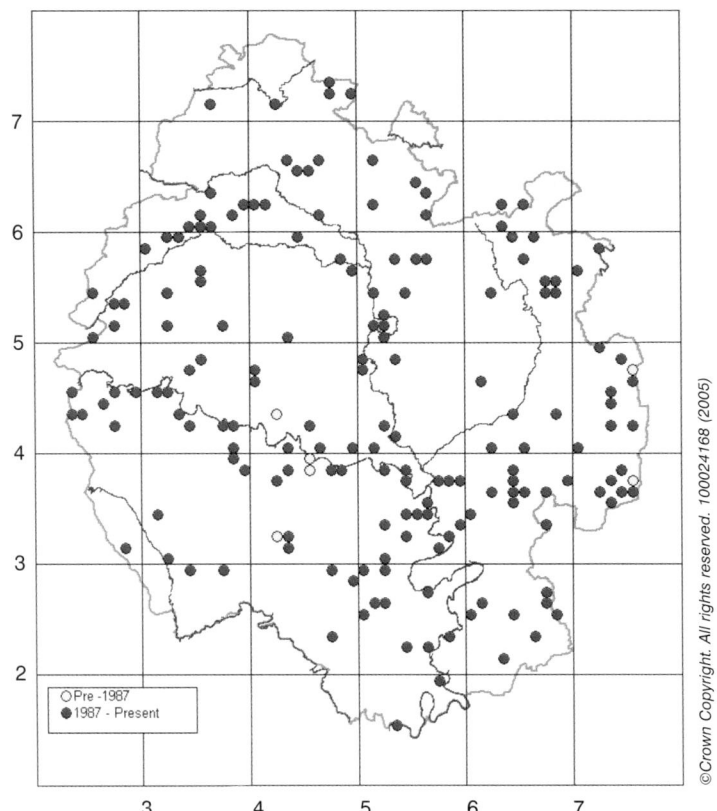

Legend:
- ○ Pre -1987
- ● 1987 - Present

Habitat

All sizes of lakes and ponds, and along canals and ditches provided they are unpolluted and sunny, less frequently, by rivers. It can be found however, on the gravel and shingle margins of the Wye in late summer.

Both sexes, but more typically the females, can be found well away from water hunting along hedgerows or over banks of brambles at the woodland edge.

Description

They are only likely to be confused with Ruddy Darters. There are several migrant darters which could turn up in Herefordshire and these could be difficult to distinguish from the Common Darter but, despite more frequent records nationally they are very rare in Herefordshire.

The red of a male Common Darter is brick-red, whereas that of a male Ruddy Darter is blood-red, almost scarlet. Females are harder to tell apart. I always rely on leg colour. The legs of both sexes are dark with an obvious yellow stripe along their length, all Ruddy Darters have black legs. It is normally easy to see this feature, especially with close focusing binoculars.

Freshly emerged males are yellow and difficult to distinguish from females; they tend to fly away from the water during this phase. Just to complete the confusion, very mature females dull to a greyish colour and can become even reddish with age. The otherwise clear wings of both species take on a rusty yellow tinge when very mature.

Common Darter – female

Behaviour

As with other darters the Common Darter spends more time stationary than in flight. It acquires a prominent perch from which it will launch attacks on intruders to its territory, often returning to the same twig or bent leaf. This can be of great assistance to a photographer; it is possible to set up the camera and focus on the perch with the insect absent, then click the shutter when it returns.

When hunting, away from water they adopt the same tactic of 'darting' from a prominent perch to grab prey then return to the same perch. At the pool the Common Darter will fly in a haphazard but direct flight close to the surface of the water. They will fly in a rapid and purposeful manner for several metres around the edge of a large pool or lake and criss-cross over the surface of a small pool.

They love to sit, sometimes with spread wings extended partially in front of them, on flat surfaces such as paths, large stones, broad branches or fence posts. When the sun loses some of its strength as summer fades these darters choose flat surfaces that are very light in colour: paths, fishing jetties, baked silt or river mud, the branch of a dead tree stripped of it's bark and blanched by the sun. On one occasion, I found several basking on the sheaves of maize cobs.

Very late in the year it is keen to garner whatever warmth it can from the sun; ancient grey specimens of indeterminate sex (by colour) can be found facing the sun on gate posts, stone walls, tree trunks and the like. (*See the back cover*).

The Red-veined Darter *Sympetrum fonscolombii*

Red-veined Darter – male

Flight Period

A migrant species which can occur at any time from the end of May until September or possibly even later than that.
I have recorded this species four times at the same site in Herefordshire:
28-08-98; 01-06-02; 02-06-02 and 14-07-02.

Status

National
An annual migrant to this country, having occurred more frequently and in greater numbers over the last 10 years. It is most often seen in southern counties where it has bred and there is a suggestion that colonisation is occurring.

Herefordshire – 1/30
The August '98 and the July '02 records were for single females, but the records for early June 2002 were of several (6 – 10) males. At the time I was very surprised by this early date and the number of individuals but I have been assured by Mike Averill[1] that the date was not unusual for the arrival of migrants and that they do not travel singly.

---

1   B.D.S. recorder for the Midlands

Red-Veined Darter
Sympetrum fonscolombiii

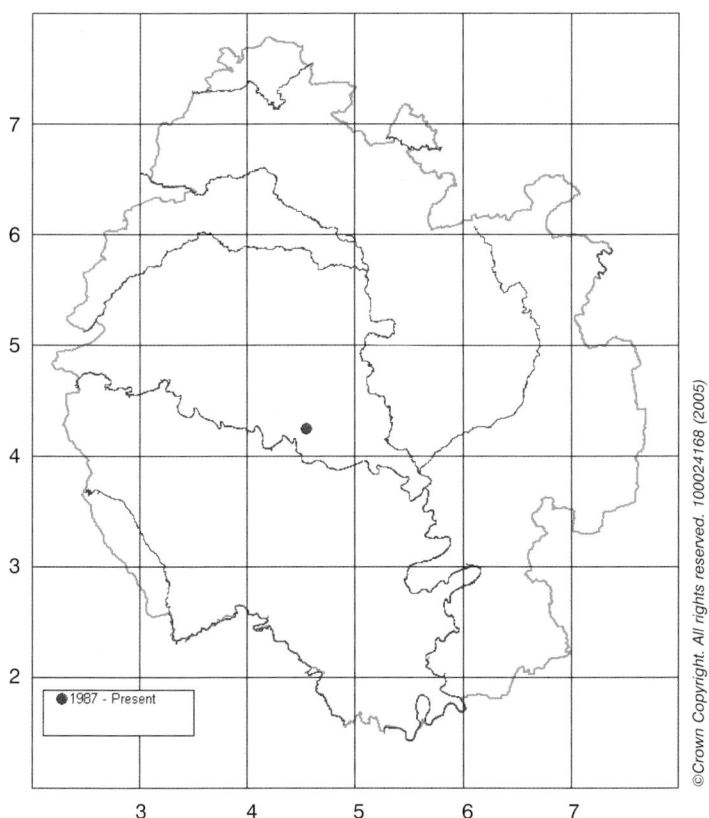

Habitat

Red-veined Darters were all recorded at Stretton Sugwas Gravel Pit. Here there are considerable expanses of bare ground covered by a mosaic of shallow pools, some of which are quite extensive and many have sparce, spikey, emergent vegetation such as Willow seedlings, rush, spike-rush and horsetails.

Description

My first encounter with this species was a remarkably bright chalky yellow female. It attracted my attention because of the colour and its size - slightly larger than the Common Darters that were much in evidence at the time. I studied this dragonfly for half an hour, sometimes from a couple of metres, through close focusing x10 binoculars. I made the following notes:

- Saffron colouring at the bases of the wings was very noticeable – a little at the base of the fore wing and quite extensive at the base of the hind wing

- The pterostigma was conspicuous – pale yellow with a black border
- The abdomen was clear yellow except for a short broken line on segment 8 and 9
- Eyes were dull buff/brown above and blue/grey below
- I could clearly see the black line above the frons descending well down the sides of the eyes
- The legs were mostly black but they had a thin yellow line on them

When I next saw this species it was at the same gravel pit four years on and this time there were several and they were all males. I was astonished to see a red dragonfly – obviously a darter – so early in the summer.

The red is pinker than the other darters (it could almost be described as magenta) and it is every bit as bright as the scarlet of the male Ruddy Darter. The features that enabled me to confirm identification, other than the pinky red abdomen were:

- The eyes were red above and greeny blue below
- The thin black border of the frons extending down the sides of the eyes
- The pterostigma is pale yellow bordered with black. This is a very easily distinguishable diagnostic feature
- The veins in the wings towards the costa were conspicuously red
- There was just a faint suggestion of a bluish tint to the wings
- The bases of the hind wings in particular were yellow
- Viewed from the side the abdomen looked squashed with thin black lines on the lower half of each segment running down its full length
- The thorax was red and downy.

The female that I saw in July of the same year did not have the same bright, chalky yellow look of the 1998 female, but was a yellow-ochre colour instead. I knew immediately it was a Red-veined Darter because I had a clear view of the black bordered pterostigma.

Behaviour

The first female I saw was relatively inactive, but the males were constantly dashing low over the shallow pools. They frequently stopped and perched on low vegetation or the ground, but were very quick to take alarm and fly off when I approached them. I returned to this site the following day with Les Clarke, the photographer, and the two of us suffered terribly from frustration before he was eventually able to get some good shots. Every time he got into position and lowered the camera towards the insect it jetted away just as he was about to close the shutter!

While all this was going on we both noticed how long they remained hovering, stationary over the same spot, but never when they were close enough for us to take a photograph!

The Ruddy Darter *Sympetrum sanguineum*

Ruddy Darter – male. Note the black legs and waisted abdomen.

Flight Period
The Ruddy Darter flies from the end of June until the end of September. It is most abundant in July and the first week of August. There are just three October records.

Status

National
Common over most of southern and eastern England, ever increasing numbers of sites (especially near the coast) in Wales and surprisingly – given its south-easterly distribution in England – it is widespread in Ireland.
The resident British population is "topped up", almost annually, by migrants from continental Europe.

Herefordshire – 29/30
Widespread across the whole county, but generally in lower numbers than Common Darter.
   Despite its ubiquitous nature the Ruddy Darter is a relative newcomer to Herefordshire[1]. When Parker recorded Dragonflies in the county in 1977 it was not anywhere to be seen.
   Having been shown my first Ruddy Darter by Roger Maskew, following his first Worcestershire record[2] in 1983, I found one at Mathon Gravel Pit on 20th August 1986. I found none in 1987 then in early August 1988 there were several at this site – probably the first breeding colony.

---

1   John Wood recorded Ruddy Darter in Herefordshire at Devereux Park at the turn of the century, but this was a very surprising and 'one-off' record – Woolhope Naturalists Field Club (1954).
2   On the Worcestershire/Gloucestershire border close to the River Severn, north of Tewkesbury.

Ruddy Darter
Sympetrum sanguineum

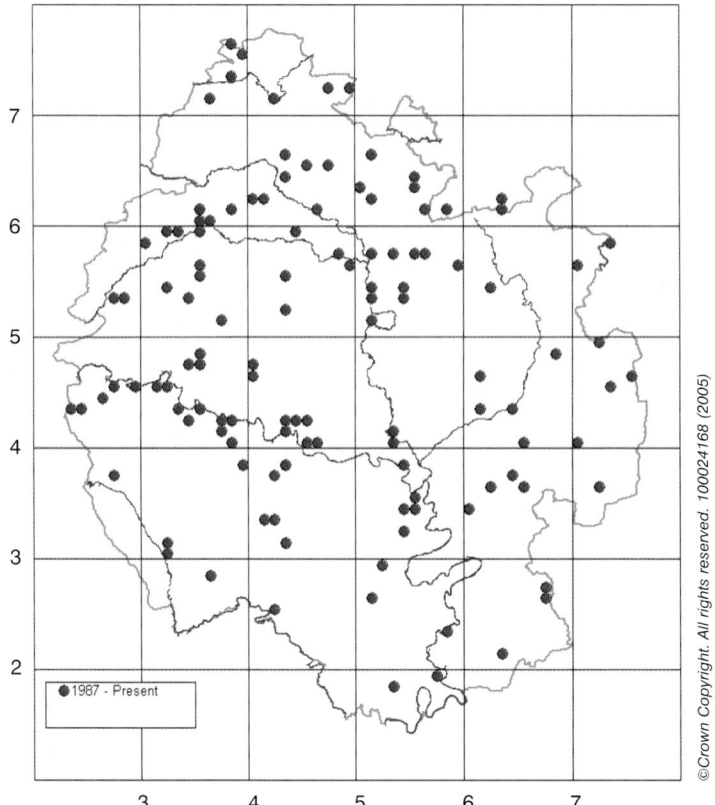

● 1987 - Present

In September 1993, when reviewing in the 'Flycatcher' the progress I had made with dragonfly recording in Herefordshire I wrote[3]:

"This darter has a south-easterly distribution in the UK with very few isolated records for Wales. However, it has been extending its range north-westerly at a rapid pace in the last ten years. In Gloucestershire there was only one 10km square record in 1979 – now there are 19! Ten years ago the Moccas record would have been exceptional – it now suggests that the Ruddy Darter could and probably will turn up in many other places in Herefordshire."

A truly prophetic note!

Habitat

Ruddy Darters like relatively small pools or sometimes ditches with emergent and marginal vegation. Trees that can provide shelter without shadowing the sunlight are ideal.

---

3 Garner P.G. 1993

There is a strong association across the county with Ruddy Darter, Emerald Damselflies and Water Horsetail, *Equisetum fluviatile*.

Eg	Jay Pool	SO3975	Winforton Field Pool	SO2945
	Oxbow – Criftinford	SO4271	Mathon Gravel Pit	SO7345

Description

The male is a small red and black dragonfly, slightly smaller than its close relative the Common Darter. The red abdomen of a mature male is a deep, bright scarlet which is

Ruddy Darter female. Note the black legs

conspicuously different from the orange or brick red of the Common Darter. Until one is familiar with the colour difference one can also note the 'waisted', club-shaped nature of the abdomen. Furthermore it has a red face framed by a thin black line which extends from across the frons down the sides of the eyes. The final 'clincher' which holds true for both sexes is the pure blackness of the legs.

When shown well, sat splayed on a light coloured surface, it is an excitingly beautiful insect.

Females, which are not waisted like the males, are much more difficult to separate from female Common Darters. Leg colour is the safest way: if the legs are all black it is a Ruddy. As with the Common, immature males are the same colour as females.

Behaviour

Ruddy Darters are much less likely than Common Darters to hunt away from water. This probably explains why on some pools, where both species breed, only Ruddys can be seen throughout much of July *(see introductory note on Darters)*. They are also more likely to perch amongst emergent vegetation than above on a prominent, exposed perch.

Their flight is flitting and jerky, stopping to hover briefly then jetting away at another angle. They less frequently make the longer more purposeful flights of the Common Darter.

The Black Darter *Sympetrum danae (previously scoticum)*

Black Darter – male

Flight Period

A very late emerging dragonfly which is most likely to be seen in August and September. All my sightings for Black Darter in Herefordshire have been in September. Observations from outside the county would suggest they stay on the wing as late as Common Darters.

Status

National

With a predominantly north and west distribution the Black Darter can be found commonly in northern England, Wales, Scotland and most of Ireland. It also occurs in pockets of suitable habitat dotted across the rest of the country, with strong populations on the lowland heaths of southern England.

Herefordshire – 1/30

Due to a lack of suitable habitat I have only found this species at one site in Herefordshire. It has been present at Peeler's Pool in The High Vinnalls (SO4772) on each of four visits that I have made during the recording period.

Such regular occurrence does suggest a small breeding population, but this pool is close to known breeding sites in Shropshire (eg Boyne Water on Brown Clee Hill (SO5977)). Given that only singles have been observed, and these have been on dates towards the end of the flight season, it would be highly speculative to describe Black Darter as a breeding Herefordshire insect.

Black Darter
Sympetrum danae

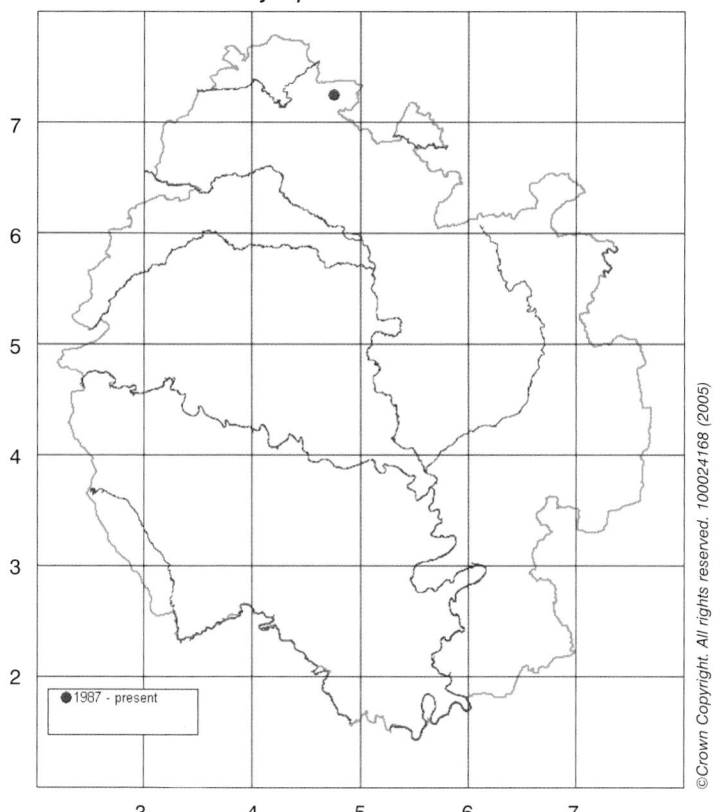

● 1987 - present

Habitat

This darter prefers acidic lakes and shallow ponds with boggy edges – typically with Sphagnum moss. Often these are heathland or upland ponds surrounded by gorse, heather or bracken.

As with the Ruddy Darter the male stays close to the water and spends much of its time resting amongst the marginal or emergent vegetation. At the High Vinnals, half of Peeler's Pool is covered with sparcely growing rush and spike-rush species. Unfortunately, other parts of the pool are covered with New Zealand Pigmyweed *Crassula helmsii*, which might render the pool unsuitable for any Dragonfly species if it is left unchecked to spread in its typical "Trifid-like" manner.

Description

This is the smallest British dragonfly and the male is the only black one. From above, the head, thorax, waisted abdomen and legs of the mature adult males are all sooty black. The wings are clear with a black pterostigma. Looking from the side there are two yellow stripes on the sides of the thorax and yellow spots along the sides of the abdomen. The females and immature males resemble more closely their Common and Ruddy counterparts. Although like the other two, the female is a yellow dragonfly with black markings, it is darker than Common and Ruddy females, and it has a very distinctive black triangle on the top of the thorax.

Black Darter – teneral male

Behaviour

The Black Darter is not aggressively territorial and is surprisingly tolerant of human observers. By easing my hand very carefully up against a male at High Vinnals I was able to nudge it onto my finger, where it remained for several seconds before I gently coaxed it back onto the plant.

Their flight is similar to that of Ruddy Darter but they do tend to hover for longer over one spot before moving on or alighting.

The Black Darter is generally considered to have good powers of dispersal but it is rarely found in atypical habitat. After 20 years of recording in Herefordshire I can assure readers that if you come across one at your garden pond or in any other Herefordshire pond it will be a most unusual and noteworthy occurrence.

This table shows the earliest and latest dates for each species during the recording period 1987 - 2005

Species	Earliest Date	Location	Latest Date	Location
Beautiful Demoiselle	4/5/90	Sapey Brook SO7256	15/8/94	Tramway Pool - Lyonshall SO3256
Banded Demoiselle	13/5/90	Sapey Brook SO7256	30/8/98	Wellington G.P. SO5047
Emerald Damselfly	13/6/92	Mathon G.P. SO7345	19/9/98	Mathon G.P. SO7344
White-legged Damselfly	19/5/02	R. Wye - Ross SO5925	6/8/00	Bromyard SO6654
Large Red Damselfly	14/4/03	Little Dewchurch SO5432 (3)	21/8/02	Titley Court SO3359
Red-eyed Damselfly	27/5/05	Devereux Park SO6236	18/8/02	Queen's Wd. Dymock SO6727
Azure Damselfly	1/5/00	Hollymount Pool SO5622	3/9/99	Trenewydd Pool SO2550
Variable Damselfly	Only 1 sighting	Berrington Hall S05162 (4)	only 1 sighting	
Common Blue Damselfly	3/5/99	Mathon G.P. SO7345	21/9/97	Clenchers Mill Pool SO7335
Scarce Blue-tailed Damselfly	28/5/01	Stretton Sugwas G.P. SO4442	8/8/03	Stretton Sugwas G.P. SO4442
Blue-tailed Damselfly	7/5/90	Mathon G.P. SO7345	21/9/97	Clenchers Mill Pool SO7335
Common Hawker	7/8/97	Brampton Bryan SO3671	14/9/96	Peeler's Pool SO4772
Migrant Hawker	26/7/90	The Gullet Quarry SO7638	30/10/91	Hartleton Water SO6425
Southern Hawker (1)	29/6/95	Croft Bank - Mathon SO7544	18/10/97	Netherton SO5226
Brown Hawker (2)	19/7/89	Eastnor Castle Lake SO7337	10/9/99	Whitbourne Hall Pool SO7056
Emperor Dragonfly	28/5/03	R. Wye - Glewstone SO5622	3/9/99	Trenewydd Pool SO2550
Hairy Dragonfly	Only 2 sightings	only Pre. 1987 records.	only 2 sightings	only pre 1987 records.
Club-tailed Dragonfly	13/5/90	Sapey Brook SO7256	27/7/96	Holme Lacy SO5534
Golden-ringed Dragonfly	8/6/95	Woodside H.N.T. Res. SO5515 (5)	26/8/91	Brilley Green SO2648
Downy Emerald	25/6/95	Woolhope SO6236	15/8/96	Woolhope SO6236
Four-spotted Chaser	28/5/02	Stretton Sugwas G.P. SO4442 (6)	19/8/97	Stretton Sugwas G.P. SO4442
Broad-bodied Chaser	6/5/01	Eastnor Castle Lake SO7336	31/8/97	Mathon G.P. SO7344
Black-tailed Skimmer	29/5/05	Stretton Sugwas G.P. SO4442	5/9/99	Mathon G.P. SO7344
Common Darter	17/6/00	Stretton Sugwas G.P. SO4442	26/11/95	Ragged Stone Hill - Malvern SO7536 (7)
Red-veined Darter	1/6/02	Stretton Sugwas G.P. SO4442	28/8/98	Stretton Sugwas G.P. SO4442
Ruddy Darter	17/6/00	Kenchester Pool SO4442	15/10/94	Mathon G.P. SO7344
Black Darter	4/8/03	Peeler's Pool SO4772	14/9/96	Peeler's Pool SO4772

All records are mine except those marked.
1. I have been told of November sightings at Stoke Bliss in recent years including 2005, but I've received no specific details.
2. See note under "Flight Period" in the species account for The Brown Hawker.

3. Phyllis King.	4. Matthew Oates	5. Michael Bradley
6. Chris Wells	7. Tony Simpson	

References

Averill M. 1996. The Dragonflies of Worcestershire. Published by Mike Averill, 25 Oakhill Avenue, Kidderminster, Worcestershire DY10 1LZ.

Askew R.R. 1988. The Dragonflies of Europe. Colchester: Harley.

Brian A. and Harding B. 1997. A survey of Herefordshire Ponds. Herefordshire Nature Trust Journal – The Flycatcher No. 65 September 1997.

Corbet, P.S. 1962. A Biology of Dragonflies. London: Witherby.

Garner, P.G. 1993. Herefordshire Odonata. *The Flycatcher* No. 59.

Gibbons B. 1999. Dragonflies and Damselflies of Britain and Northern Europe. Country Life Books: Hamlyn.

Hammond C.O. 1977. The Dragonflies of Great Britain and Ireland. London: Curwen.

Holland S. 1991. Distribution of Dragonflies in Gloucestershre. Cheltenham: Toddington Press.

Lucas W.J. 1900. British Dragonflies (Odonata) London; Upcott Gill.

Merritt R., Moore N.W. and Eversham B.C. 1996. Atlas of the Dragonflies of Britain and Ireland. HMSO.

Moore N.W. and Corbet P.S. 1990. Guidelines for monitoring of Dragonfly Populations, Journal of the BDS. Vol. 6 (21-23).

Nelson B. and Thompson R. 2004. The Natural History of Ireland's Dragonflies. The National Museums and Galleries of Northern Ireland.

Parker D.M. 1978. Survey of Dragonflies (Odonata) in Herefordshire. Transactions of the Woolhope Naturalists Field Club: Volume XLII part III.

Peers M. 1985. The Dragonflies of Radnorshire. Herefordshrie and Radnorshire Nature Trust journal – *The Flycatcher* No. 43 – April 1985.

Powell D. 1999. A Guide to the Dragonflies of Great Britain. Arlequin Press.

Prendergast E.D.V. 1997. Evidence of breeding in Odonata; a personal view, Journal of the BDS. Vol. 13 (29-30).

Simon H. 1972. Dragonflies. New York: Viking Press.

Taverner J., Cham S., Hold A., et al. 2004. The Dragonflies of Hampshire. Pisces Publications/NatureBureau: Newbury, Berkshire.

Wickstead A.R. and N.I. 1983. Journal of the British Dragonfly Society Vol 1. No. 2 (page 26).

Woolhope Naturalists Field Club 1954. Herefordshire (Chapters written to celebrate the centenary of the Woolhope Naturalists Field Club).

Recommended Reading

Brooks S. and Lewington R. 1997. Field Guide to the Dragonflies and Damselflies of Great Britain and Ireland. British Wildlife Publsihing. (Revised edition 2002).